INFERTILITY SUCKS!

INFERTILITY SUCKS!

Keeping it all together when sperm and egg stubbornly remain apart

Beverly Barna

CONTENTS

Acknowledgments 11

Chapter one
Help! I Wanna Childproof My House—
Not Myself! 14

Chapter two
But We Keep Screwing—
And Just Getting Screwed 24

Chapter three
Are You Telling Me That A Cloned Sheep
Can Have A Baby And I Can't? 44

Chapter four
It's All Your Fault: Keeping Your Marriage Together
When Sperm And Egg
Stubbornly Remain Apart 52

Chapter five
OBsession And Other OBstetric-Envy
Disorders of Infertility 56

Chapter six
Putting the Jinx on Infertility Witchdoctors 66

Chapter seven
What's Up Doc?
(Besides My Patience and My Feet?!) 86

Chapter eight
A New Take On The Boob Tube For
Those Without Breast Pumps 102

Chapter nine
The Green, Green Frog and The Blue, Blue Browns,
And Other Tales To Soothe
The Pregnantly Paused Soul 110

Chapter ten
    Happy Endings For Women Who Can't Get (Baby)
    Fat And Don't Feel Much Like Singing 128
Chapter eleven
    Cut-It-Out Cutouts 134
Epilogue
    Guaranteed Epidural-Free 138

For the woman who is tired of somber, unsolicited and scholarly advice on the matter.

"If these vaginal walls could talk, they would scream."
The Canned Pregnancy Credo

ACKNOWLEDGMENTS

F irst and foremost, I thank my husband, Michael, for staying with me through this ordeal. Not the book—that was the healing process; through the infertility. I'm sure that many marriages buckle under the strain and never recover. We certainly strained, but we never strayed. And for that, I'm eternally grateful.

I'd like to thank my family, immediate and extended, for their support. To my mother, Selma Goldrosen, thanks for always being there. I know these past years have been hard on you, as well. I hope the publication of this book brings you many smiles.

To my father, Seymour, thank you for teaching me the value of not being a quitter. You taught me that life is about finding ways to make things work when nothing seems to be working.

Notwithstanding the mother-in-law jokes scattered throughout this book, I also thank my in-laws for their quiet and kind encouragement as Mike and I battled our infertility problems. God knows, not everyone is so patient; and so do those who read and relate to this book.

Lois and Scott Winston, thanks for helping to make my vision for this book a reality with your talents. May they take you far and bring you joy.

To Ronni Sayewitz, thanks for reviewing the manuscript and offering your encouragement and advice. It was really nice of your dog to leave the room so you could laugh—and come up with Jordan.

To Wendy Janus, there are no words, not even from me. For once.

To Margaret Wilesmith: Legally change your name to Magic Wordsmith and everything else will fall into place. Even Darrin Stevens thinks so.

To Paige Stuhr, LCSW, thanks to you, as well, for your positive feedback on the book. You can tell your clients it's finally here, and I hope it helps.

To the Weiss Family, thanks for all your help, friendship and inspiration. We'll have pizza and play ball with you anytime.

A special note to Laura G. Thanks for calling pregnant women "@#$%!" in our very first conversation. Your honest admission of anger and frustration proved to me that I was on the right track with this project and helped me get it into the hands of those who need a break from that notorious roller coaster ride.

Gary Press, you're the best brother my mother never had.

Finally, thanks to all those too numerous to mention, who helped see me through my infertility ordeal and into happier times.

CHAPTER ONE

Help! I Wanna Childproof
My House—Not Myself!

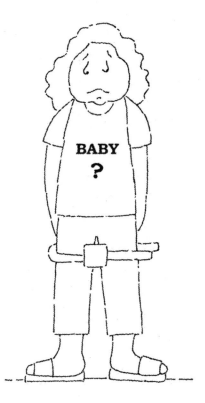

Tired of Throwing Up Your Hands—
And Your Legs? Join Us!

Lots of self-help books purport to offer insights and advice on infertility. But the best medicines for this underestimated, under-diagnosed and overall most misunderstood of all conditions are humor and brutal honesty:

I f you ever wanted to scream—or actually have screamed: *"But you don't understand what I'm going through!"* this is the book for you.

It all started in Bloomingdale's. There, amidst the invigorating, optimistic scent of new leather handbags, just around the bend from the "Up" escalator leading to untold Bloomies booty, was a taunting, stomach-churning sight: rack upon rack, row upon row, of neatly stacked "Pregnancy Survival" kits—a plethora of prepackaged maternity trinkets, a miasma of maternity mirth, marketed as remedies to the challenges of pregnancy, but in reality, mere precursors to the endless stream of cute things over which pregnant women and new mothers alone can claim dominion.

As if pregnant women don't have enough perks already. How about a survival kit for those of us who can't get—or can't stay—pregnant?

Hence, this book. Welcome to Canned Parenthood (CP), the simpatico sister you can turn to as you navigate through the Gerber goober mess that passes for reality in the distressing and depressing times in which we live. We here at CP are all too familiar with your plight. And we're seriously devoted to easing your senseless suffering. We will be honest—more so than your doctors—because we will tell you right up front that we cannot help you get pregnant. But we will also be your rude, crude companion through all your worst thoughts, fears and anxieties about the Perpetually Pregnantly Paused state we share.

If you find a laugh anywhere in these pages, we'll have achieved our goal: helping others to cope with infertility—and the fertile world around them—through humor. The exercise is not unlike whistling past a graveyard. Call it laughing past the Maternity Ward—a crucial skill for the woman who has somehow found herself in a home that is childproof in all the wrong ways.

If you have found yourself bearing a cross, instead of a child, we are fellow travelers on this lonely, twisting, always uphill road. This book is an attempt to find a place where the road curves gently downward, where pungent, large-petaled flowers dance in the air and land on the sidewalk beneath our feet, and a canopy of branches arcs overhead, a leafy lattice-work rendering the sky a tapestry of green and blue. Most of all, it's a place in the road where we will not be overrun by smug, self-satisfied pregnant women pushing strollers stuffed with cherub-cheeked toddlers into our path. Want to come along?

Note To The Fertile Civilian

A brief disclaimer for the non-infertile (or easily offended) reader:

If you, by chance, have ventured into this tome and find yourself mortified by its contents, please bear in mind that it was not written for you. It was written for your infertile friend, daughter or sister-in-law, for whom you can never seem to find adequate or appropriate words of comfort.

Next time you want to say something to her but aren't sure how or what, give her this book instead. And whatever you do, refrain from giving her your two cents at the same time. Unless you're a walking, talking fertilized egg that's ready, willing and able to climb into her womb, affix itself there and gestate for the next nine months, she has little use for your input right now.

If the person you're concerned about means that much to you, put your feet up (first of all, this will help you relate to her, as she is frequently in this position of late), and gather the intestinal fortitude to read up. You may find this book to be a great eye-opener and—more to the point—an even better mouth closer. And for that, your friend, daughter or sister-in-law will be most grateful.

Warm Regards,

CP

Canned Parenthood

Putting Things Into Perspective—When Life Hangs In The Balance of the Speculum

> Diamond earrings are
> acceptable in lieu of
> CZ promises.

Divine Secrets of The No-No Sisterhood:

Had it with infertility? The poking and the prodding, the ceaseless examinations and endless questions about the most intimate aspects of your life and your body? And that's just from your friends and family, who are "trying to help!"

Here at Canned Parenthood, we have the Perpetually Pregnantly Paused thing down cold. We'd say we had it "down to a science," but that phrase has somehow lost its cache for us in recent years. Nevertheless, we're pleased to share with you herein some of the insights we've gleaned along the road to being Perpetually Pregnantly Paused.

(Yes, we know that "perpetually pregnantly paused" does not in the least flow trippingly from the tongue; why should describing the condition be any easier than living with it? And while we're at it, we detest the word "flow." It reminds us of getting a period—a wretched notion. "My friend?" My ass. And we don't like to think about tongues, either. That makes us think about sex. And guess where that leads us? Right—right back to being Perpetually Pregnantly Paused—still. It's a rotten trap.

Since we at Canned Parenthood are such very kind and sensitive soul sisters, we offer the following additional options: the point-blank "Pregnot" and the more alliteratively alluring alternative: Not Knocked-Up. Feel free to use these terms as interchangeably as faux fertility specialists despicably use their desperate denizens.)

Now, back to our numerous insights: First, it's crucial to recognize that with infertility comes a certain power. We must seize it. For example, we alone have proof that God is a white male. We know this because if God were a woman, the rest of us would have everything we wanted. Ann Taylor sales would coincide with our pay periods, when our checkbooks are bloated, and not our menstrual periods, when our stomachs are bloated.

We would get depressed from buying minivans, which painfully represent the disappointing state of our counter-cultural myths; not from buying mini-pads, which painfully represent the disappointing state of our pharmacy counter myths. The notion of infertility would be as unthinkable (we at CP use the word "inconceivable" only advisedly) as going to the ballet on Super Bowl Sunday.

And if God were a minority, He would understand the importance of seeing to it that everyone had an equal shot at attaining our culture's most cherished prizes: pregnancy and parenthood. Anyone who has been infertile for any amount of time knows that this is far from the case. There is nothing fair about who becomes pregnant and who does not. And infertility remedies are as effective in leveling the playing field as are affirmative action remedies: We may be able to make the numbers look better. But underneath it all, someone is always being left out, in spite of all the good intentions.

Since God is a white male, His reasoning is hence inscrutable, or perhaps non-existent, depending on whether he once belonged to a college fraternity, is currently involved in a fantasy football league, or insists upon leaving the toilet seat up. We should, therefore, not waste our time trying to figure out why he has done this to us. It will never make any sense.

Second, we must learn to appreciate that there is power in the unknown. Yes, we can fret and roil in frustration over not knowing whether we will ever conceive. But isn't it so much healthier to revel in it? In fact, Canned Parenthood prescribes for all of us a new status: We are not infertile, childless or child-free. There is nothing free about this roller coaster ride. In fact, the tickets are quite costly. And there is no freedom in not having that which one desires most. But we will overcome, even if our husbands' sperm and our eggs do not go over easy.

Look at it this way: We are enjoying a prolonged state of marriage without kids from a sophisticated vantage point. Don't get hung up on the fact that you arrived here through no choice of your own. That's something your kids would one day complain about as teenagers, when arguing with you over taking out the garbage.

Pity—don't envy—people with children. After all, you may eventually have a family. They have already shot their wad, so to speak, and are now left to deal with the consequences, not all of which travel down the road of life cutely dressed and rolling merrily along the sidewalk in brand-new strollers (which, incidentally, can cost a fortune). These include, just to name a few of the more onerous things, three-o'clock feedings, diapers that smell like sewage treatment plants and college funds. And oh, yes, the latest moronic iterations of those ever-popular Beanhead Babies, Tele-Sappies and Toddler Mutant Alligator Pukers.

As you've been going through your own ordeal, your child-burdened friends and family have no doubt stumbled over many a child-rearing error along with many a Tonka Truck. They have already done the dirty work of researching child care options, pediatricians and the implications of breast-feeding vs. bottle-feeding and public vs. private schools. If you should one day

19

become a parent, you can avail yourself of all their hard-won knowledge. If you don't, think of all the hassles you'll have avoided. While your friends are stuck smelling the diapers—and eventually, no doubt, the pot—you can remain free to stop and smell the roses.

So, next time you see a pregnant woman, kick back and have a martini. With extra olives. Toast her as she looks longingly at your cocktail. Sashay by with the best body you can muster in the highest heels you can navigate. Wax buff with a Brazilian bikini wax; let's see *her* get into that position! Zip past those nerdy minivans in a zesty little two-seat roadster convertible. Glory in the romance of driving with the top down, unencumbered by clunky child-safety seats, no three-week stale Cheerios crunching beneath your feet. Now, who's envying whom?

Some Of My Best Friends Are Pregnant

Pregnant woman so
beatific. Not beautiful.
Who had sex with her?

Even the sweetest infertile woman is likely to develop profound feelings of jealousy when her futility is seen in the context of others' fertility.

Everything about pregnancy, child birth and children is way too big and ubiquitous—ostentatious, even. Pregnant women are enormous. Their husbands are doting, gloating puffed up lumps of testosterone-fueled pride.

The state of pregnancy carries with it not only the promise of an angelic neo-nate, but also an ungodly buzz. When a pregnant woman enters a room, all talk turns to talc. Ruminations on epidurals, sonograms, breast pumps and morning sickness eclipse all else. Who among us but a pregnant woman would brag about vomiting to the worshipful nods of the adoring assembled masses?

Diaper bags, bottles, rattles, drool and other such post-natal paraphernalia orbit around the nuclear family tableau, confirming the chaos theory's efficacy. Minivans clog the streets and obscure our view. Strollers clog the sidewalks and obscure our passage. Babies and children are inordinately loud and conspicuous. And their grandparents are even worse. It's enough to make a Perpetually Pregnantly Paused woman scream like a woman undergoing hard labor—which, in her own way, she is.

While so many women—some mere girls!—push and breathe, directed by their Lamaze instructors and urged on by their husbands, the Perpetually Paused woman just holds her breath. She watches it all go by, like a motorist stranded on the highway, fascinated by the technology that allows thousands of other cars to move, while she remains stuck, immobile due to invisible forces beyond her control.

The right perspective can help put you into the driver's seat— if not controlling your destiny, at least preserving your sanity.

Doing Well While Doing Without

Nipple rings are cool
when on someone else's kid.
Next comes tuition.

A mantra a day keeps the blues away: A helpful and healthy reminder that not everything is blissful about childbirth and parenting:

There comes a time in every woman's infertility drama when every pregnant woman is a "bitch" and every wailing bundle of diapers is a "damn baby." Try to calm yourself and put things into their proper perspective by chanting the following soothing mantra over and over again: Hemorrhoids, stretch marks, episiotomy, Menendez, hemorrhoids, stretch marks, episiotomy, Menendez, hemorrhoids, stretch marks, episiotomy, Menendez . . .

Maintain a positive outlook: I once consoled myself by thinking that this ordeal would be something I could some day tell my grandchildren about. But I soon realized the folly of that notion. I also know, however, that there is little chance that anyone will ever call me "Bubbie," which is a good thing.

You may also find solace in the notion that perhaps your fecund foe fought infertility herself before giving birth. And it's helpful to remember that someday that cute little baby will be a rotten teenager—perhaps one who is in need of intense psychotherapy and who needs the jaws of life to remove her nose/nipple/genital/tongue rings. And of course, when that time comes, everything will turn out to be her parents' fault. When she outgrows that phase, she will go to an expensive Northeastern college. Soon after, her family will have to pay for a big wedding.

Studies show that it can cost hundreds of thousands of dollars to raise a child for the first 17 years. Next time your home pregnancy test comes up empty, plunk down a few thou on a new sofa. No guilt allowed. Your house will soon look great. No sticky kids to mess up all your nice new—or antique—stuff. Imagine the excitement you'll derive from spreading the word about your own impending very special blessed event:

> *"Guess what Aunt Joan?!—I'm expecting . . . A*
> *new couch! Due in four to six weeks, no money down,*
> *no interest for six months! I think it has your coloring.*
> *I hope you can join us to welcome it into our home."*

And just think, you'll never have to worry about putting the sofa through college. If none of this helps neutralize your non-natal neurosis, get down to basics: Arrange a trip to the mall with a friend who has small children (the more the messier). On one such outing, the agony of lunch in the food court (sticky tables, sticky trays, sticky food, sticky kids; strollers galore, much whining, little dining—absolutely no wining—vintage or Boons Farm Wild Strawberry, for that matter) was followed by a stroll through the mall, during which my friend's 4-year-old son asked incessant questions, including these, directed at me: "Where's *your* baby? Do you have a *baby*? *Where's* your baby? . . ." I thought I was rehearsing a scene for a horror flick with a tiny Lee Strasberg.

This interrogation was briefly interrupted when the mini-method actor's 2-year-old sister, with no ado, lifted her dress over her head and whipped off her diaper—in front of Brooks Brothers, no less. Fortunately, the diaper was devoid of any solid waste at the time.

As I pondered the possible wisdom of containing toddlers through the use of Hannibal Lecter travel-wear, my friend chased after her chapping cheeked child, soggy diaper in one hand, clean emergency provisions in the other, the 4-year-old running ahead, laughing uproariously and *still asking questions*, I sauntered into Brooks Brothers to check out a great sale.

Minutes after we parted company, it occurred to me as I soared across the turnpike on-ramp toward my mellow, sweet smelling abode, that my friend was probably still in the mall parking lot, fussing with a stroller, child safety seats and Barney good behavior bribes.

"You Can't Always Get What You Want," Mick Jagger consoled me from 105.9 F.M. "You Can't Always Get What You Want," he repeated, singing, it seemed, directly to me. I turned it up—*way* up. "But if you try sometime, you just might find— you just might find—*you get what you need!*" Oh yeah; indeed. (Odd that these lyrics should come from the highly, um, *prolific*, much jaded Jagger, who seems to have no trouble at all helping to bring children into the world.)

Once home, I tossed my pre-natal vitamins into the kitchen garbage bin. Yes, I ultimately bought another bottle. But I shall remember that day the next time a pregnancy test comes up negative. And I might even smile.

CHAPTER TWO

But We Keep Screwing—And
Just Getting Screwed

The Biological Clock Crock

Ovary young, what
will you leave us this time. We're
39 once. Twice?

A reality check for the childless woman: You are getting older. You may be getting better. But you definitely are not getting more fertile. The solution? Take it like a man.

O ur culture has a way of distorting everything that passes through its giant myopic lens, and infertility is no exception. Those of us who are living with the reality of infertility are further alienated by a faux language that doesn't accurately reflect our experiences—as if we didn't have enough trouble. Our sizable strife gets lost amidst the pointless balloons of misinformation that cloud the stratosphere of social discourse.

What we need is a seasoned, reasoned dialogue. What we get is Catie Cutesy cooing over the McCon septuplets—as if every infertile woman is just this close to popping out a jackpot of Mini-Mes.

The deception starts early and is oft repeated. In fact, one of the most severe cases of cultural sleight of hand is embedded deep within our social and medical lore: We do not have biological clocks.

What we have, in reality, are biological *calendars*: A clock will mincingly tick off tiny, innocuous seconds one by one by one. And an alarm will buzz when a predetermined, finite point has been reached. Clocks can be manipulated. Think about daylight savings time. What's an hour, give or take, of daylight? If women really had biological clocks, wouldn't we be forever tinkering with saving an hour here, a few minutes there, in the desperate hope that we could become pregnant? Calendars, with the isolated exception of leap years, offer no such false hope and flexibility.

A calendar will casually, stealthily lop off weeks and months and years at a deceptive and capricious clip, as another menstrual cycle, birthday and New Year's Eve skate breezily by. A clock lets you know just where you stand at any given moment—literally. But a calendar will roll over like a friendly old dog, waiting for a belly rub, only to crap on the carpet when you finally get around to paying him some long overdue attention.

What this means in the infertility game is that you do not have precious time to waste, nor should you tolerate, encourage or abide anyone who tells you otherwise. For all too soon, your biological calendar will move on—not like sand sifting slowly through an hourglass, but rather like the Tasmanian Devil devouring all the varied fruits of the jungle in his mad and reckless path.

This is not to suggest that society is intentionally singling us women out for unfair treatment. If the ability to bear children was tied to the male body, and not the female body, things would be very different. But our culture would still find ways to warp perceptions about the impending end of the cycle of fertility.

For example, instead of the misnomer "biological clock," we would hear incessantly instead about the biological finish line. Wild, Bacchanalian Women-A-Pause feasts would dominate the cultural landscape. Men would proudly down Viagra, along with her-moan replacement therapy, to keep their breasts small and their mustaches large. Special micro-brews would be developed with which to toast the great milestone. Block-long bonfires would consume unneeded tampon boxes and unused rubbers, as newly liberated men danced around the flames, beating libidinous drums and other appendages. Those fortunate enough to achieve this rite of passage during Super Bowl week would be feted, revered and lionized like—well—like new mothers.

Infertility would become hip, and known instead as The Pause That Refreshes: There's nothing wrong with Pausing on the way to menopause, society would infer; it's just different, an alternative, perhaps, even, a choice. We're not stuck; we're doing our research. We're not morning sick, mourning or pining away. We're not getting stretch marks. Not getting fat. Not getting our vulvas stretched like limousines. We're Not Knocked-Up. And that's OK.

So much, you see, depends upon attitude. CP's (not too PC) prescription? Take it like a man.

MAN-aging Your Biological Calendar

Lesson One: Be Decisive. Do not, even for a moment, entertain the notion that you may be wrong (about this or anything else). No self-respecting man would ever express self-doubt.

You probably realize by now that the only appropriate response to any doctor who tells you to "Just go home, relax, have sex every other day after the tenth day of your cycle and you'll be back here pregnant in just a few months," is to join us in wishing him a waiting room full of patients with very smelly feet, a serious aversion to hot wax and an undying belief that, someday, it will be proven that the yeast that makes yeast infections so richly pungent is actually a cure for cancer, AIDS and the hiccups. Ditto the doctor who tells you to try to conceive for a year before determining if you have a fertility problem.

Call it women's intuition. Call me an impatient, irrational bitch. Just don't call me late for the Maternity Ward—which you will likely be if you fail to act decisively on your suspicions.

Lesson Two: Don't be coy about checking out the women. Real men don't eat with their mouths closed. And they don't hide their curiosity about their intended quarry—or the competition.

Checking out the other women in your doctor's waiting room

will help you to recognize the sure signs that you are in a legitimate infertility clinic: You are surrounded by women who look like they could be pregnant, except that they look miserable, not contented. It stands to reason. You see, this group of bloated galley slaves is retaining not only water, but also rather mysterious looking shopping bags, filled with used syringes, needles and drug vials—the paraphernalia of the paranormal rites of fertility in our modern times.

Other tip-offs: The waiting room magazine selection is suspiciously, albeit happily, bereft of back issues of *Parenting*. And finally, a certain perverse calmness pervades the inner office. Chalk this up to the minute degree to which the office staff must deal with insurance carriers, as we all know that 99.9 percent of them will not cover infertility and related expenses.

Lesson Three: Check out the equipment. Real men are always on the look-out for the latest technological advances and gadgets.

The astute observer will notice some sure signs that she is not in a legitimate infertility clinic. Any *schmuck* can print up a business card or hang out a shingle promoting the fabrication that he or she is an infertility specialist. But beware of the dog: If your doctor does not have transvaginal ultrasound equipment, an embryologist, an IVF lab and a bathroom full of *Penthouse* magazines, you might as well be in Fred Flintstone's cave munching away on an Upside-Down-Flint-Rubble-Bubble Cake. A plethora of posters proclaiming newborns' birthdays and birth weights are likewise a likely sign that your doctor is running a baby factory, not a home for the non-nursing.

Lesson Four: Don't take any crap. After all, real men never do. Why should you?

Perhaps the only thing worse for an infertile woman to encounter than a baby factory is an IVF factory. These are comprised of doctors who are more concerned about their own fertility statistics than they are about the welfare of their infertility patients. To them, a bird in the hand is no different than two birds in the bush—or anything else in the bush, for that matter—a sensitive point, indeed, when yours is the bush in question. A doctor who immediately suggests that you undergo an IVF cycle without: a) first determining your overall physical condition; and b) discussing the costs, risks and efficacy of IVF, must be suspected of having had his fingers crossed behind his back when he was reciting the most honorable and much defiled Hippocratic oath. Put another way, he's probably talking out of his ass while scrutinizing yours.

Bottom line: Run and hide from any doctor who seems more interested in processing your hide than in saving it. This is no time for false bravado.

Bloated Top Ten Lists

In a restaurant
sorrow visits our table.
Toddler misbehaves.

In a restaurant
a brief reprieve from our pain.
Toddler misbehaves.

Each of the following lists actually harbors more than ten entries. But we here at Canned Pregnancy believe deeply in adding more stuff to the world in whatever ways we can dream up. You know how it is: infertile body—fertile mind.

The Top Ten Situations That Prove That Infertility Is More Annoying Than Anything Else You've Ever Experienced

How infertility stacks up against other stressful situations:

1.   Trying To Finish A College Term Paper The Night Before It's Due

How they're similar: You're surrounded by stacks of research. You know that everyone else has already completed the assignment and is kicking back in the pub, celebrating their accomplishments. (How you hate it when they parade around campus, showing off the products of their labors.) You have no idea how things are going to turn out for you. And of course, the stress is elevated to nosebleed status by the haunting reality that you're running out of time.

How infertility is easier: No footnotes and bibliographies.

How infertility is a lot worse: I bet whatever you ingested to stay awake for your all-nighter was much cheaper than fertility drugs and didn't require injections and indignities. And no one else really cared all that much whether you finished your term paper.

2. Getting A Flat Tire

How they're similar: You experience that lonely, picked-upon, "Why me?" feeling of frustration and helplessness. It's only natural to look around at everyone else progressing speedily and effortlessly down the road, while you remain hopelessly stuck. It's lonely to see so many people all around you, and yet to remain so isolated.

How infertility is easier: You're not necessarily at high risk of being hit by a passing car.

How infertility is a lot worse: People may come along to help. But who knows if you can trust them, or if they'll rip you off at the first opportunity? Being stranded on the side of the road does not require constant blood tests and transvaginal ultrasounds.

3. Having A Bad Blind Date

How they're similar: You try to get as much information as possible about the situation, but ultimately, things are pretty much out of your hands. You agonize over the unknown.

How infertility is easier: You can't be disappointed in someone who never shows up.

How infertility is a lot worse: A bad blind date can be nipped in the bud within an hour; infertility can drag on for years.

4. Having A Huge Fight With Your Mother-In-Law

How they're similar: Your family's future is at stake, and possibly that of your marriage, as well. Emotions are running high and there's a lot of crying. In severe cases, screaming may also be involved. In the worst instances, everything ends in utter silence.

How infertility is easier: Your husband isn't torn by dual loyalties.

How infertility is a lot worse: You can't keep house, cook *or* deliver grandchildren? Her poor son.

5. Coping With An Obnoxious Boss

How they're similar: Your days are chronically darkened by the presence of a powerful specter over which you have virtually no control. This demon can make your life miserable—*and* it can have a direct and lasting impact on your finances.

How infertility is easier: If you're working with the right clinic, your doctor will demonstrate a lot more care and sensitivity than your boss will ever be able to muster.

How infertility is a lot worse: Your boss may have all the charm of a hypodermic needle, and his criticisms may indeed be harsh, but he can never get under your skin and really sting you like, say, a Lupron injection can. And, while going into your boss's office may sometimes feel like a bloodletting, you will, in fact, always leave his domain with the same amount of blood with which you arrived. If this is not the case, put this book down immediately and go find yourself a good labor lawyer post haste! (God knows, you may never need a labor doctor; the least you can do is have yourself a decent career.)

6. Fighting With Your Insurance Company

    How they're similar: In both cases, the benefits you seek are at best elusive, and often unattainable altogether. There's little discernable rhyme or reason to the way things are working out—or failing to. You think you're doing everything "by the book" and yet it's all for naught. Tons of red tape and random frustrations have you asking, "Why the hell does this have to be so damn complicated?"
    How infertility is easier: It isn't perpetuated by a bunch of mindless, faceless "suits." (At least, we don't *think* so.)
    How infertility is a lot worse: It's the difference between fighting City Hall and fighting Gulf War Syndrome: The insurance company is a vast bureaucratic machine, which will try to explain in writing why it won't deliver on its promises. Not so with infertility. No one can explain why you can't deliver on the promise of motherhood. Your foes are as nebulous and mercurial as a swarm of infertile angels dancing on the head of a sterile needle.

7. Getting Stuck Behind A Really Slow Driver When You're In A Really Big Rush

    How they're similar: YOU JUST WANNA *SCREAM*, DAMN IT!
    How infertility is easier: Taking drugs is actually legal.
    How infertility is a lot worse: The slow driver will eventually turn right (albeit while signaling left). Infertility is more like getting a bogus ticket for a "rolling stop," while a drunk

driver swerves around you going 75 miles an hour on a rural street on his way home for a peaceful, uninterrupted sleep.

8. Waiting For A Furniture Delivery

How they're similar: No matter what you plan for or expect, you will be wrong every time.
How infertility is easier: No one will sweat all over your house (except for those times when you yourself are experiencing hormone overload). And no tipping is required.
How infertility is a lot worse: Your furniture will arrive eventually, and it will be more affordable than an IVF cycle.

9. Hanging In While Growing Out A Hideous Haircut

How they're similar: Both require a tremendous amount of patience.
How infertility is easier: It's not right there on top of your head.
How infertility is a lot worse: Wearing a hat will not help, although you will surely encounter people who insist that it might.

10. Being Pulled Over By A Cop

How they're similar: The minute you realize what's happening, you get that inimitable "I'm screwed" feeling, followed closely by the realization that you have been unfairly targeted for rotten treatment, when many others who deserve to be punished are getting off scot-free, instead. (What about the guy who cut in front of everyone at the toll booth, and the bimbo who smokes crack and gets pregnant?)
How infertility is easier: You might not be breaking water

anytime soon, but at least you're not breaking the law, either. *How infertility is a lot worse*: If you flirt with the cop, you may well get away without a ticket. If you flirt with your husband, you may well get sex. And a period, which itself can feel like a citation.

11. Being In A Fender Bender

How they're similar: Oh shit! But not fatal.

How infertility is easier: The other "driver" involved in the entangled, hideous mess in which you find yourself is your spouse. If you guys wind up exchanging insurance cards, license plate and drivers' license numbers, your problems dwarf that of infertility. Call a marriage counselor, not the cops.

How infertility is a lot worse: Who do you blame? Not even the best of lawyers can help you recoup for this nightmare.

12. Living With Noisy Neighbors

How they're similar: Both irritations, over which you have little or no control, go right to the heart of your lifestyle. When the party booms, when the lawn mower whines, when the dog barks all night—these are a few of our least favorite things, and so is the Pregnot plight.

How infertility is easier: Your family is way too small to seriously add to the neighborhood noise problem, so you can rest assured that you will never be the butt of counter-complaints. And no one will be able to take your grievances out on your kids when the time comes for Boy and Girl Scout fund-raising drives and Halloween.

How infertility is a lot worse: You'll always have to pay someone to cut your lawn, while your noisy neighbors can rely on their own kids for free. At the same time, your tax dollars pay for public education, even though the kid might do a crappy job on your lawn because he has to rush home to finish his homework.

13.   Putting Your Foot In Your Mouth

How they're similar: You'd do just about anything for another chance to get it right.
How infertility is easier: Hey, it's not your fault! You're the victim of circumstances.
How infertility is a lot worse: Most everyone has embarrassed themselves at some point in time. But very few people can empathize with the plight of the Perpetually Pregnantly Paused. A self-effacing blush can mitigate the damage caused by foot-in-mouth disease. But if an infertile woman blushes, everyone immediately assumes she's: a) angry at seeing yet another pregnant woman with children; b) overdoing her fertility medications, or c) having a hot flash. They will then try to tell her that she can become pregnant by putting her foot into her mouth.

Top Ten People, Places and Things to Avoid

Common nouns and other annoyances from which the Pregnantly Paused woman is strongly advised to take un-maternity leave:

1.   Pregnant women

2.   Pregnant women who continuously rub their bellies (actually, equivalent to the above entry)

3.   The typical Ob-Gyn waiting room (often chock-a-block with the above)

4.   Anyone under the age of 10

5. Doctors whose waiting rooms are strewn with back issues of *Parenting* magazine

6. Doctors who tell you, "Just relax and you'll be pregnant in no time"

7. Baby showers that drown you in sorrow

8. Baby namings and christenings

9. The baby food aisle in the supermarket

10. The Pampers and Huggies aisle in the supermarket

11. Pre-schools

12. Elementary schools

13. Birthday parties for anyone under the age of 16

14. Maternity wards

15. Maternity stores

16. The baby department in department stores

17. Playgrounds

18. Mall food courts

19. Any restaurant that gives out birthday balloons or has aisles clogged with lines of strollers

20. People who can never find babysitters, because they don't know how to plan

21. People who can never understand why you still don't need babysitters, because they don't know how to listen

22. People who themselves will always need babysitters, because they will never grow up—even if their kids eventually do

23. Kids for whom you once babysat, who ask you to baby sit for their kids.

Top Ten People, Places and Things to Find

Uncommon nouns and other treasures the Perpetually Pregnantly Paused woman is strongly advised to seek out while on un-maternity leave:

1. Other infertile women

2. Really wise women (those who are wise enough to know when not to try to give advice)

3. A doctor who is a true infertility specialist

4. A time and place to cry in peace

5. A time and place to talk calmly to your husband

6. A time and place to talk hysterically to your husband

7. A time and place not to talk to anyone (but yourself, if you so desire)

8. A time and place to laugh alone

9. A time and place to laugh with friends

10. A place to hide a stockpile of home pregnancy test kits

11. An exercise routine you like

12. A time and place to vent, Vent, VENT . . .

13. A way to indulge in an expensive and totally unnecessary accessory

14. A time and place to wear it

15. A star to wish on

16. Time to learn George Carlin's seven dirty words you can't say on television. They come in handy when it's time to vent, Vent, VENT; and women with kids don't get to say them!

Top Ten Stupidest Things That Have Ever Been Said To Infertile Women

A real-life compilation of the worst of the worst:

While not scientifically compiled (as you know, we at Canned Parenthood have our own thoughts about the usefulness of science these days), we believe this list can be an invaluable resource for those who think they know the stupidest people on earth. All of the following examples are based on actual conversations:

1. What are you two waiting for? (Frequently uttered by in-laws.)

2. We feel really bad about what you're going through, especially now that we have our own baby and realize how

wonderful parenthood is. (Frequently uttered by former friends.)

3. If you prayed more often, you'd get pregnant. (Frequently uttered by mothers who wish to be grandmothers.)

4. Maybe you should stop riding your bicycle. (See above.)

5. I hope your career is worth the sacrifice. (Frequently uttered by maiden secretaries.)

6. Don't you want children? (Frequently uttered.)

7. If only you hadn't waited so long . . . (Frequently uttered by former gynecologists.)

8. I'm sure it's for the best; if you had a baby, it would probably be deformed. (Frequently uttered by the kind of petty, pious people who give God a bad name.)

9. You know, the first commandment is, "Be fruitful and multiply." (See above.)

10. There's no such thing as being "a little bit pregnant." (Frequently uttered by various cliché spewing folks. Anyone who has ever had a miscarriage knows that this is a lie.)

11. Isn't that house too big for just the two of you? (Frequently uttered by neighbors with too little house and too many kids.)

12. Would you like to come to our child's birthday party at Discovery Zone? (Frequently uttered by utter idiots.)

13. Wow! You're like, a real career gal! (Frequently uttered by younger, pregnant co-workers.)

14. Do you want to see my stomach? (Frequently uttered by utterly idiotic pregnant women.)

15. You know, we weren't even trying to get pregnant this time. (Frequently uttered by parents of large families.)

Top Ten Terrible Truisms Of Pregnotsy

Some Pregnantly Paused days are worse than others. Infertile women can count on unfortunate coincidences like these to really rub their noses in someone else's bag of dirty diapers:

1. The most obnoxious person you encounter in your doctor's waiting room in any given month will become pregnant.

2. The woman you most detest will announce her pregnancy to you on the very day that you get your period following yet another unsuccessful cycle.

3. One day, your friend is bending your ear about her sister, who's hooked on drugs and heading for a divorce. Ten months later, your friend breaks your lunch date, because that same sister has given birth to a beautiful baby girl, whom she must get to the hospital to gaze upon.

4. The most irritating people with children you see while waiting to board a plane will be seated in the closest possible proximity to you on the plane itself. Needless to say, the brats will carry on like animals throughout the entire flight. And the kids will be a big pain, too.

5. When celebrating a special wedding anniversary in an

exclusive restaurant, the maitre d' will guide you to a romantic table beside a cozy fireplace. But the very next table will harbor a talky 7-year-old, whose voice can be heard in Hades. You resist the urge to feed her to the flames, but must insist on another table, where her voice is a mere 20-decibel distraction.

6. While waiting on "hold" to speak to your doctor about your latest infertility imbroglio, you will be treated to radio broadcasts reporting on such things as pandas in captivity getting pregnant through IVF.

7. You are promoted and given a much larger, more prestigious office. So, you're not a Mom. At least you're a success in other ways. The woman who is hired to replace you moves into your old office. She's four months pregnant. And a bitch to boot. Finally, a pregnant woman occupies your space.

8. You try your best to ignore the baby at the next table during lunch at your favorite weekday haunt. But she is mesmerized by your very existence. Out of everyone in the entire restaurant, you're the one with whom she chooses to make extended eye contact and at whom she will giggle incessantly. Her mom thinks it's just the cutest thing. And, truth be told, so do you. On one level. But down in the basement of Id, you desperately wish they'd both go away and leave you to enjoy your Oriental Chicken Salad and grown-up lunch companions in peace. The whole thing makes your teeth hurt, and you're not even teething. How about a nice glass of house wine to go with that whine?

9. Few things in life can match the sublime irony of being infertile and having to take birth control pills to moderate your hormones in preparation for an IVF cycle. What's next—free Rogaine treatments from your electrologist?

10. While you can still have sex anywhere in your house, any time of day or night, it will get you absolutely nowhere.

11. Stressful circumstances will often stymie your efforts to successfully complete an IVF cycle. Not only can't you seem to win the game, you can't even get past "Go"—or even get sent to jail, for that matter. Here are just a handful of things that can cause cycle-interruptus:

> ovarian cysts
> periods missed
> lab inspections
> vaginal infections
> not enough eggs
> government regs
> doctor's away
> insurance delay
> appointment confusion
> pregnancy illusion
> lab construction
> alien abduction
> unruly ova
> a supernova . . .

I once had an IVF cycle interrupted because my doctor's lab was being refurbished. (This turned out to mean new wallpaper and waiting room chairs, to the best of my knowledge—but alas, no new waiting room magazines.) Anyway, following the two-month long construction project, a test had to be performed in which mouse embryos were exposed to the lab environment. If the embryos survived intact, the lab was deemed safe for IVF. If not, more tests—and more waiting—would be in order.

A nurse called the day the results came in, to report that the mouse embryos hadn't survived. I decided immediately to face up to the reality with grace and maturity. These are, after all, circumstances beyond my control. It's not the end of the world, just a temporary setback. There's always next month. And besides, why should a damn mouse get pregnant when I can't?

12. Hark! You finally complete an IVF cycle and everything works. Alas. Nothing worked.

CHAPTER THREE

Are You Telling Me That A Cloned Sheep Can Have A Baby And I Can't?

BAAAAA!

> They say life's not fair.
> We can attest to that fact.
> Morons procreate.

On the fundamental unfairness of infertility:

T he following infertility rhyme is proudly displayed in the CP waiting room. Feel free to make it your own as you struggle to come to terms with your Pregnant Pause:

> *One may be evil, illegal, a scoundrel—a beagle!*
> *Wife beater or cheater,*
> *Bird, bee or mosquiter.*
> *One needn't be married or planning to wed,*
> *Un-harried or thoughtful to bed,*
> *Disease-free or nice,*
> *One may even have lice –*
> *Just don't be infertile instead.*

Yes, Vagina, there is a Santa Claus. It's just that he may never send a baby down your particular chimney, in spite of the fact that you've heeded all prior warnings about being naughty and nice. Finding coal in your uterine stocking year-in and year-out? Don't blame yourself.

The painful truth is that many perfectly horrible people are able to procreate with ease, while many worthy and wonderful Mom and Dad wannabe's toil away on infertility's front lines, often retreating with not so much as a teething ring to show for it. If these vaginal walls could talk, they would scream. One can only wonder what Darwin would have to say about this sad, sad state of affairs.

It's bad enough that we're surrounded by pregnant women every day. It's worse to read about pregnant teens murdering their newborns for fear of what the neighbors might say, should they give birth at too tender an age. There are no IQ or SAT tests one must pass prior to becoming a parent—much less a Bar Mitzvah, Bar Exam or Medical Board. No kindness quotients are tallied, no maturity indices weighed.

Among those having children are people who cannot successfully complete drug tests, driving tests, sentences (prison or grammatical), the alphabet and appropriate responses to wedding invitations. None of this matters. And nobody can tell you why—not even Canned Parenthood. Not even, in all likelihood, your doctor—who is, after all, just the real-life equivalent of the man behind the curtain in the Wizard of Oz, frantically pushing buttons and pulling levers to achieve the desired effect, but in the end, a mere mortal, every bit as confused about life's mysteries—and the mystery of life—as you and me.

We can bitch. We can moan. We can bitch and moan. We can bang our heads against the wall of the latest, greatest infertility treatment. But alas, we cannot change fate. Life *is* unfair. We must and we will come to terms with the terms and conditions set out for us. But first, we will groan. And then we will vent. And everyone in our path is fair game to be ground under the imaginary wheels of the wheelchair in which we will not be riding to and from the Maternity Ward.

The day-to-day reminders of life's fundamental inequity are harshly punctuated by the glittery presence of celebrity pregnancies—a particularly irritating class of pregnant vs. Pregnot unfairness. Strange-Change Action Jackson's a father. Alleged pedophilia and actual parenthood: Perfect Together. Cher Boney was married to Gregg All-Man for about three minutes. They had a kid. Tony (Odd Coupling) Allbran wed a young thing when he was 70-something. He sired a child. And then another!

Two Spicy Meat Girls inconceivably conceived, seemingly simultaneously—talk about pouring salt on the wound. Even Dolly, the cloned sheep, had a little lamb. Baaaaa! I didn't even know she had a biological clock!

Poor Demised Di and her Frisky, Finicky Prince could do nothing right in their ill-fated marriage—except create an heir and a spare, pronto, by royal command. I tried that once. All I got was a sharp gas pain and an old tire around my waist.

"Lady" Madonna's a mother in what appears to be just another trendy image alignment. Or perhaps—with children at her feet—she's merely trying to meld her legacy with that of The Beatles, in which case, may we recommend she try instead to tout peace on earth, the banning of land mines, or at the very least Bed Peace.

Kids and pregnant bellies it seems, make great props. Demi-Goddess More-More, who can always be relied upon to flag a dubious trend, ushered in a new age of pregnancy chic by posing au natural while oh so prenatal on the cover of *Vanity Squared* magazine. Naturally, other pregnant celebs, including Candy Craw-Mommy, followed her lack-of-suit.

Here at Canned Parenthood, we have logged numerous complaints from women who have flipped open seemingly harmless copies of *People* magazine only to see a severely pregnant Mademois-Elle MacPherome, coyly sporting a milk mustache, while massive doses of hormones course through their veins, threatening to provide them with mustaches that are all too real.

Ah, but take heart, dear, dismayed Paused one. From the annals of celebrity lore also comes this gem: Norma Jean couldn't cook up a baby in her Baker, either. That's right; the beautiful, talented, icon-who-married-other-icons, Kennedy-hopping, sexuality popping Marilyn Monroe was reportedly Pregnantly Paused—the most glamorous in a long line of wonderful women unable to improve upon nature by reproducing: indicating that some of us have reached genetic plateaus, perchance?

Relax, *Cherie*, Darwin would be proud. You're not merely infertile, or even Perpetually Pregnantly Paused. You're fully evolved.

Infertility and Injustice: Tracing the Roots of Women's Oldest Complaint

Darwin's theory says
we evolve until perfect.
Guess we have it right.

A really old—yet rarely disclosed—history lesson puts things in the proper perspective.

We are reminded time and again that pregnancy—be it among the rich and famous or the *schlub* next-door—is a key component of the natural course of events for most women. We the Pregnantly Paused may never know why we were singled out for exclusion. But reviewing the condition in light of its historical perspective may provide some insights and possibly even some relief:

Our sense of injustice is a natural, fundamental emotional reaction that harks back to the Stone Age, and a great-great-great-great-great-great-great-ancestor, who was the smartest, most capable person—male or female—in her tribe. She could hunt. She could fish. She could be dragged by the hair with the best of 'em and still look great at the end of the day. But for her, there would be no cozy family cave, no darling little savages to raise.

All her talent, all her intellect, all her beauty, meant nothing. Until she vowed to take charge of her destiny. She did not stop merely at popularizing the safari, the leopard-skin print, the fishnet stocking and the ride-through theme park zoo (after first having invented the wheel, of course).

No. It was, in fact, she who created the art of hieroglyphics. Naturally, you're curious as to how this came to pass. We at CP have obtained critical documentation that proves that this great-great-great-great-great-great-great-ancestor of ours (no descendants, of course) developed early communication as we know it.

Failing to initiate a menstrual cycle at the appointed time of month, our Fore-Mother (an honorary term, if ever there was one) became hopeful that she was at last bearing a child. When this failed to happen, and when the failures mounted up time and time again, she began, in her immense frustration, to throw rocks at the walls of her humble, solitary cave-condo. The resulting designs—so full of passion and raw emotion—were immediately hailed as art that was worthy of being shared with the hearts and hearths of the homes of the tribal leaders of the day. A star was born, along with a new means of communication.

Many others soon followed in her footsteps—even though her prehistoric toes were very large—using cave walls to communicate their thoughts, feelings, daily travails and victories, and finally, their family histories. In this way, in her day, our great-great-great-great-great-great-great-ancestor became quite the celebrity in her own right. How big, you wonder? Think Princess Diana. The bitch was huge—even without the tragic ending and the legacy of a couple of cutie princes!

This, of course, did not stop our heroine's friends and neighbors from trying to tell her what she was doing wrong when it came to the problem of procreation: Perhaps, they opined, men didn't tug hard enough when dragging her by the hair; perhaps she wore her loin cloth too tight, or spent too much time walking upright; perhaps what she really needed was to take in a small Velocorapter to satisfy her maternal instincts and help her to relax. Our foremother fore-bore this onslaught with uncanny patience: You see, she recognized that it's human nature for folks to be unable to relegate themselves to minding only the goings-on in their own caves.

You are no doubt wondering why you have never heard about this wise and talented woman before. Actually, you have, although, with no direct descendants to call her own, her legacy was never accurately disseminated until now.

Our Fore-Mother's family name was "Lincoln." But caveman grunting being what it was, and the lazy masses not having changed much since ancient times, this was soon shortened in the vernacular to "Linc." When Miss Linc failed to procreate, some of the crueler of the locals insisted on interminably prattling on about all that she was missing by not participating in motherhood. The snide remarks stuck, and Miss Linc soon became known around the jungle as "Missing Linc."

And so it is that today the Missing Link, though widely respected in her time for inventing the safari, the leopard-skin print, the fish-net stocking, the ride-through theme park zoo, the wheel and hieroglyphics, is best known to us not for all of her achievements, but rather for her heretofore unexplained hereditary disappearance. Unfortunately, her infertility eclipsed any accomplishments for which she might otherwise have been recognized, a situation with which every infertile woman can relate. We can only hope that such uncivilized behavior will pass—in just a little more time.

CHAPTER FOUR

It's All Your Fault: Keeping Your Marriage Together When Sperm And Egg Stubbornly Remain Apart

Remember When Playing Doctor Was Fun?

My husband's sperm swim
a frenetic little dance.
Egg's a wallflower.

*When your husband's sperm count wins the "Golden Stirrup Award"
and you are the obvious infertility culprit; a word or two for the would-be
Madame Ovary:*

B eing an infertile couple sucks. Being the party responsible for that infertility sucks even harder. They say that one-third of all infertility cases originate from problems with the male, one-third are rooted in problems with the female and one-third are unexplained. There are some answers to life's mysteries that we may well be better off not knowing. This may well be one of them. In fact, CP would argue that 100 percent of infertility cases should be classified as unexplained, for in the end, that is truly what they are.

In keeping with CP's philosophy of always looking for the secret benefits of infertility, however, we offer the following perspective: Those women who become pregnant as a desperate means of saving their failed marriages have it all wrong. If they were to feign infertility instead, their hubbies would stick to them like nicotine patches. Infertility is simply one of those things that—if it doesn't tear you apart—will bring you much closer together.

Think about it: How many women can say they've been in a room with their husbands while another man maneuvers an eight-inch long probe into their vaginas? And not one of them is deriving the slightest bit of enjoyment out of it.

Infertility will strain your marriage like a Gerber pea. If you can trust your husband to stick an inch-and-a-half-long needle into your butt in your quest for parenthood, your marriage can survive anything. Among the special moments we share: early Sunday morning trips to the infertility clinic, watching your kitchen table turn into a chemistry lab, Lupron-induced mood swings, the battle with myriad medical woes and insurance foes, the emotional highs and lows that are the very hallmark of the infertility struggle.

Listen, Madame Ovary. Don't throw it all away just because things aren't working out the way you expected them to. Looking for transcendence? "Madame Ovary c'est moi." And take it from me:

I have gone so far as to offer my husband a divorce so that he may pursue normal family life with a young, fecund woman. After all, our marriage vows didn't say anything about him sticking around when my eggs run screaming off into the night at the very sight of his hapless sperm. Fortunately for me, he declined the offer.

Now I know that even though I got stuck with Teflon eggs, I lucked out in the husband department. And, unlike my Grade Z eggs, which were somehow bestowed upon me by default, I actually chose him—a Class A mate. It's nice to know that he really loves me for myself. Or maybe he really enjoys giving me those injections every month (a routine that truly gives a new, much less fun meaning to the notion of "playing doctor").

It may be that the pain of infertility strikes women harder than it does men. We are, after all, apparently hard wired—by nature, nurture, or both—to have mother boards that program us to be mothers. But battle this one together, and, come what may, your marriage will be stronger than ever. Just beware the insidious effects of too many visits to the infertility clinic. It's a sad day, indeed, when your man announces that he is tired of jerking off.

CHAPTER FIVE

OBsession And Other OBstetric-Envy
Disorders of Infertility

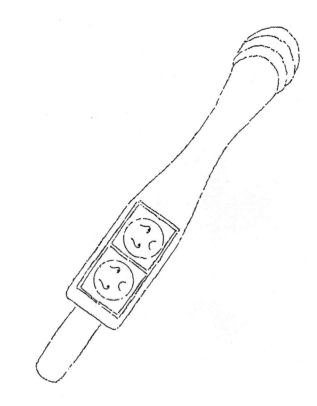

I Want To Be BIG!

Happy little bird
somewhere ova the rainbow.
Why, oh why, can't I?

How a woman can tell when infertility is making her slightly crazy:

There's nothing wrong with wishing for something. Just remember Tom Hanks' character in the movie, "Big." Choose your Zoltars wisely and cautiously, or you may be in a quandary over the outcome. Big might mean "big with child." Or it could mean the onset of the attack of the 50-foot woman. Or—and here's the clinker—it might mean nothing at all.

One of the many problems with infertility is that it's practically impossible not to obsess over. How can you focus elsewhere when you are constantly waiting for a period to start, counting the days until you ovulate, injecting yourself with a Molotov Cocktail of hormones, inserting into yourself progesterone suppositories, having sex, not having sex, giving blood when you don't want to, bleeding when you don't want to, and being subjected to transvaginal ultrasound procedures twice a week?

Everywhere you go, you're bulldozed by pregnant women, people with kids, and that most hated apparition, the pregnant woman with kids. It's nearly impossible not to be constantly reminded that you're Pregnantly Paused. But obsessing over your condition has its limits (or should). Here are some sure signs that your thwarted maternal instincts have given way to distorted neurotic impulses. (Score one free pregnancy test kit for each example that describes you.)

- You have hallucinations:
  You see cloud formations in the shapes of a uterus and fallopian tubes.
  You convince yourself that you see positive home pregnancy test results on negative tests.

- You've asked a "Magic Eight Ball" if you're pregnant—and expected a legitimate answer.

- You define any carved wooden wall hanging as a fertility god and go out of your way to caress it for luck in such public places as Thai restaurants.

- You are convinced that whenever someone you know dies, it's a sure sign that you personally will soon be chosen to replenish the population.

- You go to the doctor for a blood test *before* your period is late.

- You take a home pregnancy test *after* your period starts.

- You can't understand why Target doesn't carry home pregnancy test variety packs.

- You perceive hopeful omens from deceased relatives in ultrasound pictures.

- You see agile, swimming sperm in ceiling tiles.

- You've taken a home pregnancy test on your lunch hour.

- You've taken a home pregnancy test in a public restroom.

- You spend more money on home pregnancy tests than you do on food.

- You find God. You lose God. You find God. Your lose God. You find God . . .

- You won't let your husband have a sexual fantasy unless you're ovulating.

- In idle moments, you catch yourself thinking about baby names.

- When you're busy, you catch yourself thinking about baby names.

- You truly expect to learn whether you are pregnant from a fortune cookie.

- The sight of V-8 Juice can send you into a deep depression at certain times of the month.

- You find yourself relating meaningfully to hard-boiled eggs.

- Your first reaction when you see a pregnant woman is "Bitch."

- Your second reaction when you see a pregnant woman is "Pig."

- Your third reaction when you see a pregnant woman— well, let's just say it rhymes with "runt."

- It goes downhill from there.

- You refuse to buy a new box of tampons until you positively, absolutely have to have them.

- You really love the Stones, but listen instead to chamber

music on NPR every chance you get, because you read somewhere that hens exposed to classical music have scientifically been proven to produce more eggs.

Do you relate? It's OK. So do we. Not to worry. The day will come when we will be able to channel our energy more constructively—perhaps we'll join forces to picket fur coats—at a nudist camp in Miami. With protest signs in English. Ole! Oy vey!

Very Superstitious

When you believe in
things you don't understand then
you're grasping at straws.

Infertile women often become superstitious about conceiving. So do their friends and families. This inevitably leads to more frustration and disappointment:

I once asked a "Magic Eight Ball" if I was pregnant. "There's no doubt," it assured me. Of course, the Magic Eight Ball was right. There was no doubt—that I wasn't pregnant. Clouds are clouds. Fortune cookies are as sagacious as Triscuits. "Magic Eight Balls" are toys. Home pregnancy test kits are not.

Your friends and family no doubt contribute to the problem by trying to "fix" your infertility with a host of clever suggestions. One of the secrets to avoiding emotional burn-out at this stressful time is being able to recognize the attitudes—yours and others'— that inevitably lead to let-downs. How many of the following have you heard? Which have you actually tried?

You'll get pregnant if you . . .
. . . adopt.
. . . take pre-natal vitamins.
. . . relax.

 . . . pray.
 . . . take valerian root.
 . . . stand on your head after sex.
 . . . have sex on Friday nights.
 . . . have your husband wear boxer shorts.

I don't care if your mother wears army boots. If you believe any of this stuff, you also believe the woman at the cosmetics counter who rationalizes the ludicrous price of the moisturizer she's selling by telling you that "It lasts a really long time." Nothing that comes in a two-ounce container can last a really long time, except, maybe, plutonium, which I'm sure does little for one's complexion.

Disregard these Old (and new) Wives tales. You may—or may not—get pregnant. But you will preserve your energy, sanity and dignity.

What Color Is Your Home Pregnancy Test Kit Result? (Avoiding the Test Kit Trap)

Bloated, crampy grouch.
A period on the way?
I'll pee on a stick.

The popular book, "What Color Is Your Parachute?" has helped many people cope with career frustrations. In this chapter, CP reaches out to help women cope with a common infertility frustration—home pregnancy test kit addiction:

You can't control your infertility, but you can manage it. And you can control your reaction to it. I've wasted a lot of perfectly good urine peeing on sticks. Second only to the high cost of fertility medications in the financial and emotional expense derby that is infertility is the high cost of addiction to home pregnancy tests.

If you absolutely, positively cannot resist the urge to pee on a stick or into a cup just one more time this month, go on out and buy yourself a bunch of Popsicles and Dixie cups. It's cheaper and just as productive.

StickEnders: Hope for the Seriously Addicted

Can't kick the habit on your own? Consider joining "StickEnders." Our experts will gradually and gently wean you from your addiction with the utmost discretion and sensitivity. Beat unhealthy Pregnantly Paused habits. Meet other women who can relate to your monthly anguish. The program is strictly anonymous and highly effective. "Stick With Us. We Won't Stick It to You!"

StickEnders' methods—indeed, the very existence of StickEnders itself—has always been a closely guarded secret. In recognition of the growing number of women facing home pregnancy test kit addiction, however, the organization has decided to come out of the medicine cabinet, so to speak.

StickEnders meetings convene monthly, or more specifically, every 28 days. Each chapter of StickEnders is organized around one of four menstrual cycle patterns, so that members can join a group whose meetings coincide approximately with their own cycles. The goal is to make a regular meeting available to every infertile woman within one week of the day she expects her period each month—even if her period itself is not regular. (Special consolation and coddling is offered to those unfortunate souls whose menstrual periods typically commence on Mondays.)

Meetings are held in unmarked minivans parked in pharmacy parking lots across the country. The vehicles are identified only by the discreet presence of the StickEnders' logo on a small sticker placed on the rear driver's side bumper of the van, often beside a bumper-sticker touting the fact that the driver's kid recently made honor roll. (This, of course, is a red herring, but an effective one at that.) The small logo depicts a home pregnancy test stick— with a negative reading, of course—surrounded by a red circle with a red line slashing across the center, in the manner of the international symbol for "no-smoking."

The ruse is completed—and members' privacy ensured—by the presence of sun shades pulled over the vans' windows. (Some of the more jocular and ironic StickEnders counselors outfit their minivans with Minnie Mouse and Winnie The Pooh sun-shades and the like.) Once inside the StickEnders-mobile, of course, no signs of actual baby life are apparent.

Members prepay based on the number and variety of tests they wish to take each month. A special flat fee of $300 buys twenty tests and offers a wide array of home test choices for those who enjoy a lot of diversity with their chemistry. (If this seems costly, remember that you are not paying tax, as StickEnders is a non-profit group, and consider that Lupron costs even more and makes you feel even worse than a negative result on a home pregnancy test.)

StickEnders members are expected to bring their completed tests (as many as they like) with them to each meeting. The meetings commence with a series of optical illusion exercises, which put members in the proper frame of mind in which to review their test results. Once confronted with the reality that their minds and eyes can easily play tricks on them, they are prepared to cope with the implications of "seeing" positive pregnancy test results that aren't really there.

The home pregnancy test kit habit is further challenged when StickEnders members share their tests with objective partners randomly assigned from among the group, who are more likely to accurately assess negative test results. Confronting proof of a Pregnant Pause can be daunting, so each StickEnders meeting concludes on a high note: An optional monthly "Way-Out Weigh-In" is held to affirm that members are retaining their girlish, Not Knocked-Up figures, even if they may also be retaining fluids.

Members then return home with StickEnders' convenient video training guide to reinforce the lessons learned through group participation. The tape, "Stop The Stick-Schtick Inanity!" includes helpful and invigorating segments on:

- Spotting The Top Ten Habits That Lead To Test Abuse
- Spotting Instead of Menstruating And Its Implications For Test Abuse
- Spotting Other Test Abuse Triggers (includes tips for coping with the popular "Late Period—Early Morning Urine Sample" Trap)
- Spotting Trends In Home Pregnancy Test Kit Development (from stick to cup—avoiding the temptations posed by emerging technologies)
- TrainSpotting—When Yet Another Negative Test Pushes You to Lie Down in the Middle of a Heavily Trafficked Train Track

The video is also helpful to StickEnders husbands, many of whom suffer sympathy Pregnantly Paused symptoms, including, but not limited to, imagining positive pregnancy test results on negative tests.

If, in spite of all of the above measures, a StickEnders member is unable to control her home pregnancy test habit, she may, at the discretion of StickEnders experts and CP staff, be issued a supply of Stick-O-Tine patches, which administer regular doses of the hCG hormone to ensure a positive test result, even in the absence of an actual pregnancy. The idea is to neutralize the seductive power of home pregnancy test kits altogether, by rendering their readings completely invalid, meaningless and worthless.

This controversial emergency intervention measure is intended to shock the addict into ultimate recognition of the "emphatically empty uterine state." Her treatment is then considered successfully completed. Until the next month, of course.

CHAPTER SIX

Putting the Jinx on Infertility Witchdoctors

INFERTILITY

Coming Out Of The Infertility Closet

Nosy co-workers
want to know all about it.
Privates off limits.

What do they know and when should they know it?

S o, you're not gay. And you don't play one on TV. But
you have been wrestling with the problem of "coming
out" of the infertility closet.

At a certain point, one's family figures it out, when the
anticipated grandchildren's pictures fail to appear at the appropriate
time on refrigerator doors.

Close friends can be helpful. Or annoying, depending on
whether they say things like, "We feel really bad for you guys,
especially since Zachary was born and we know how fantastic it
is to be parents."

If things go on long enough, one's boss gets into the loop.
How else to explain all those mornings of coming into work
late, sporting a Band-Aid in the crook of your arm? And if one
pursues the plethora of high-tech treatments now available, those
sick days can mount up like a pile of McCon septuplet diapers.
For infertile women, many of whom are Type-A personalities,
missing that much work can truly make you sick.

Then there's the rest of the world: acquaintances, co-workers,
distant relatives, neighbors, friends of friends. These are the tough
ones, the ones who ask things like, "What are you guys waiting
for?" And say things like, "How old *are* you? Hey, you better get
on the stick!" Little do they know that we have spent an inordinate

amount of time on the stick—the home pregnancy test kit kind. These are invariably negative experiences.

Enough obfuscation.

Everybody out. Here's how:

First, we must caution others to refrain from asking us any and all of the following. (That goes for those who know our long-suffering husbands, too.)

Will you adopt and have you tried Doctor So and So? (Allow me to tell you where to go; and I've tried everything but Mick Jagger. I can't get no satisfaction. Period. Every month. Exclamation point.)

Have you tried such and such a treatment? (Please; I haven't taken so many drugs since college and that was a heckuvalot more fun.)

Do you know why you can't have children? (*This is often an insidious ploy to determine who's at fault, husband or wife.* We'll never know for sure. And for sure, neither will anyone else. Blame it on Rio. Blame Judge Ito. Blame all those drugs we did in college. *Finito.*)

Please do not attempt to comfort us with motivational stories about your neighbor's cousin's friend's daughter's old college roommate's boss, who got pregnant when she "just relaxed." It's way too late for that. Nor does standing on our heads help.

No, we are most adamantly not "at least having fun trying." At a certain point in this grueling struggle, infertile couples are just happy to be in the same room for the proceedings—if they are lucky enough to still want to be.

If you're pregnant, don't be afraid to tell us. We can take it. But please forgive us if we derive some perverse satisfaction from your morning sickness. We're suffering from our own brand of mourning sickness. And we can't help it if we find it a tad bit amusing that you look like a Volkswagen Beetle just drove up your dress.

Are we frustrated? For sure. Angry? Absolutely. Alone? Alas, certainly not. *American Demographics* has reported that more than 15 percent of women between the ages of 15 and 44 have tried infertility treatments. And Canned Pregnancy strongly suspects that our counterparts in the gay community can easily relate to our sense of alienation from the world of nuclear family life.

Much like our counterparts in the gay community, the Not Knocked-Up must constantly assess to whom they wish to disclose their secret circumstances. Some of these decisions are easy: Close friends and relatives who are likely to be understanding and sympathetic, and who can be trusted to remain discrete, may be taken into one's confidence relatively early on. After all, these people can offer much needed support, even if they sometimes stumble over their own good intentions in the process.

But what about the rest of the world? If you're unfortunate enough to be suffering through a protracted battle with the Fertility Gods (or Demons), there may indeed come a time when necessity will dictate that you "come out" to the world at large about why you have not come out-to-here with child.

You will find that the longer you grapple with your infertility, the more you will feel the need to confide in others about it. But the decision to make these disclosures should be made on a strictly case-by-case basis. In each instance, you must ask yourself, "Will telling this person help or hurt my ability to cope?"

Knowing whom not to "come out" to is crucial to your ability to get through your ordeal with the least amount of unwanted input from Infertility Witchdoctors and their ilk.

CP offers the Yenta Identification Process (patent pending) as a handy guide. Don't be coy about employing your "Yent-ar" (Yenta Radar) at the first sign of inappropriate behavior from a mere acquaintance. Here are the kinds of things that should trigger your Yent-ar alarm:

Someone who asks inappropriate questions about other topics can be counted on to ask questions that are at least as inappropriate about your infertility.

Someone who seems to be baiting you by endlessly talking about other peoples' babies and pregnancies probably is.

Anyone who's nosy enough to ask you when you plan to start a family is mouthy enough to tell everyone else why you haven't yet.

People who frequently glance at your abdomen during routine conversations are best avoided.

Those who suddenly develop an intense interest in the topic of adoption for no apparent reason have an apparent motive for those of us who are a-parental.

Warning: Yentas will often try to swap information with you in exchange for your confidences. Be on the look-out for those who express a sudden, sharp and spurious increase in the degree to which they attempt to communicate with you about personal matters.

Don't mistake a gossip for a girlfriend; and know the link between dishing and fishing. There is ample difference between discussing one's divorce and divulging the details of one's sister-in-law's divorce. Chances are, the chick chattering about the latter's about as reliable as a cheap paper plate laden with three-day old haddock and soggy mashed potatoes. In disclosure as in dining, always go for the good china and the best fillet.

Coping With Infertility Witchdoctors

Everyone means well.
They're only trying to help.
I wish they'd shut up.

Even if your Yent-ar is top-notch, you will profit from the following tips for living among the fertile, and those for whom your infertility has become a (way too) personal crusade. Most infertile couples lead frustrated lives of noisy desperation, fending off uncomfortable inquiries from Yentas and from family and friends who want to help but just don't get it. Two highly effective approaches to appease these Inquiring Minds are offered:

Conventional wisdom holds that there are two things one refrains from discussing: religion and politics. CP proposes that we add a third crucial item to that list: having—or not having—children. Alas, until that notion is passed into law (that which governs the social graces), the Perpetually Pregnantly Paused will surely continue to encounter those for whom the ramifications of sexual intercourse are viewed as fair game for public discourse.

For even if you can come to terms with your infertility, you will surely have to contend with others who cannot. My grandmother used to say that the world travels in pairs. With all respect to Grandma (she should rest in peace), this is actually incorrect. The world, in fact, travels in small groups, called nuclear families. Those of us who are not a part of one such unit will find ourselves excluded in ways obvious and subtle from the larger group. Thus, members of non-nuclear families are often left to feel downright radioactive. But we don't have to get blown away by this situation.

How to respond? That depends on your personality, mood, the current state of your infertility struggle (expecting to be expecting? preparing to remain Paused? contemplating adoption?) and who knows?—perhaps, your horoscope and biorhythms, too.

Flying high on an estrogen surge? Feeling magnanimous? Then follow Auntie Estradiol's prim etiquette advice. Feeling blue, bleeding red, low on life from Lupron overload? Then Miss Conception's cranky concepts are for you. Either way, you can get the upper hand when confronted by Infertility Witchdoctors and Fertile-izers.

The World According To Auntie Estradiol—Well Mannered Responses to Ill (Um) Conceived Questions

Ill-Conceived Question: What are you guys waiting for?
Well Mannered Response: Actually, we've been trying for several years and just haven't been too lucky.

Ill-Conceived Question: Have you ever considered adoption?
Well-Mannered Response: We've done some research and determined that it a) just isn't for us, *or* b) is something we might look into in the future; we're not quite ready, yet.

Ill-Conceived Question: Why don't you just relax and stop trying so hard?

Well-Mannered Response: I/We appreciate your concern, but our doctor feels that we're handling this whole thing extremely well.

Ill-Conceived Question: Have you ever been pregnant?
Well Mannered Response (If "no"): I haven't been so fortunate.
Well Mannered Response (If "yes"): I seem to be able to get pregnant, but not stay that way; it's a very painful situation for me, and I'd prefer not to discuss it.

Ill-Conceived Question: Is the problem with you or your husband?
Well-Mannered Response: I'm really not comfortable discussing such personal matters.

Ill-Conceived Question: Don't you want kids?
Well Mannered Response: I think we'd enjoy being parents; and I think we'd be great at it. Unfortunately, things just haven't worked out for us in that regard. Thank God (husband/wife) is incredibly understanding about the whole thing. It's just reinforced our whole relationship.

Ill-Conceived Question: How can you stand shooting yourself with all those needles?
Well Mannered Response: I know that parenthood often entails sacrifice, so I choose to look at the current challenge as a way to get a head start.

Ill-Conceived Question: How old are you?
Well Mannered Response: I like to consider myself timeless—and wiser with every passing day.

Messin' With Miss Conception: Snappy Retorts to Nosy Questions

Alas, we're not always capable of performing up to Auntie Estradiol's very proper standards. Next time someone gets under your skin by presuming to ask you about the inconceivable, extract them like a tiny splinter thusly: Imagine them dancing around you sporting a Witchdoctor's mask, or shoveling a pile of fertilizer—nature's own brand, of course—up to their nosy little noses.

The following are Miss Conception's suggestions for dealing in a forthright manner with those who have no manners of their own. Desperate to give 'em the finger? Try one of these zingers. Don't worry about being rude. These people have already demonstrated that they are not in the least bit sensitive.

Nosy Question: What are you guys waiting for?
Snappy Retort 1: The *next* millenium.
Snappy Retort 2: Privacy.
Snappy Retort 3: A miracle.

Nosy Question: Have you ever considered adoption?
Snappy Retort 1: Yes. We've discussed it and we'd like to adopt you and teach you some manners.
Snappy Retort 2: Yes, but nobody will adopt us; we're too old.
Snappy Retort 3: Perhaps you'd consider adopting us and buying us a child?
Snappy Retort 4: Have you ever considered a face lift?

Nosy Question: Why don't you just relax and stop trying so hard?
Snappy Retort 1: We've tried that and find that in such idle moments we tend to germinate not embryos, but rather hostile feelings toward know-it-all friends, family members and even mere acquaintances who are completely misguided in their assumptions and advice.
Snappy Retort 2: Because certain people keep annoying me. And I don't mean my mother-in-law.
Snappy Retort 3: What is it that scares you about liposuction?
Snappy Retort 4: Why don't you just relax? I hear not breathing is a great way to start.

Nosy Question: Have you ever been pregnant?
Snappy Retort 1: Have you ever been to charm school?
Snappy Retort 2: Yes. Once I was expecting twins, but (pregnant pause) one of them ate the other in my womb. (This one is a sure show-stopper. You may lose a friend. It may be worth it. Only you can decide. I swear on my empty uterus, I have used this and it was richly rewarding. Besides, I never much cared for the guy, anyway.)
Snappy Retort 3: Three times. (Defy them to ask what happened.)

Nosy Question: Is the problem with you or your husband?
Snappy Retort 1: Only my hairdresser knows for sure, but I think I will go for a full head of highlights next time.
Snappy Retort 2: The doctors aren't sure, but they have counseled me to avoid undue stress whenever possible, so please go away.

Nosy Question: Don't you want kids?
Snappy Retort 1: There seem to be quite enough small and clueless people around already. Would you like a cookie?
Snappy Retort 2: Peace on earth would also be nice.

Nosy Question: How can you stand shooting yourself with all those needles?
Snappy Retort 1: It beats shooting myself.
Snappy Retort 2: Would you rather I shoot you?
Snappy Retort 3: I have learned that penetration in all its permutations can be a good thing.

Nosy Question: How old are you?
Snappy Retort 1: Older than I look.
Snappy Retort 2: Younger than you look.
Snappy Retort 3: The sound you hear is not my biological clock ticking. It's a bomb.

And finally, Miss Conception presents a special case:
The "Not Yet" Problem

Nosy Question: Do you have any children?

This one introduces its own peculiar dilemmas. For one thing, the question would probably be considered nosy and intrusive only by someone who's infertile, with the possible exception of Miss Manners. For another, it presents different kinds of discomfort, depending on where one is on the infertility roller coaster. Someone who is relatively young and just starting to wonder if she is infertile can dismiss the question with a quick, "Not yet." The emotional discomfort may linger, but the social awkwardness will fly off with the speed of a Speedo at a Seven Sisters mixer.

The real dilemma arises, say, five years hence: One who has consumed a mountain of prenatal vitamins, yet finds herself closer to menopause than Santa Claus, will have a dilly of a time uttering the "Not yet" response. One need only imagine the doors of inappropriate reactions this could open as the interrogator tries to comprehend how one so mature can possibly be cooling her heels at such a crucial juncture. (What are you waiting for? Better get on the stick. Oh, I see . . . *wrinkle nose, furrow brow* . . . You know, my cousin Edna was infertile until she tried acupuncture and the acupuncturist slipped and poked her in the elbow by mistake and she needed stitches and she wound up having triplets and then another baby *without even trying* and on and on and on.)

How do you know when you have reached the point beyond which you can no longer comfortably employ the "Not yet" net? All Miss Conception can say is, it's one of those moments in life when a threshold is clearly crossed. You might not see it coming, but once you smack into the pane of painful reality, you emerge a different person. It's akin to suddenly knowing you're too old to sit on the laps of male relatives, to dress up for Halloween, to cheat on exams, to automatically purchase skin-care products for "oily" skin or to make a salon appointment without specifying if it's for a haircut, color or both. One just knows.

There comes a time when one has been through too many hormone injections, egg retrievals, blood tests and emotional blood baths to simply and blithely utter the words, "Not yet." There comes a time when Dr. Kevorkian seems more relevant to one's situation than Dr. Spock. There comes a time when one must wonder if saying "Not yet" to that eternal question won't evoke a counter-response worthy of Hillel: "If not now, when?"

In such cases, Miss Conception advises developing an ICP, or Imaginary Child Profile. An ICP will effectively blunt the force of unwelcome family status questions by "Giving The People What They Want." The critical components of the successful ICP are as follows:

- Gender (Oh, how nice! A boy!!/A girl!!/Twins!!!!)
- Age (Oh, how sweet!!!)
- Name (Oh, I love that name!, or Oh, how unusual!)

Everything else is optional and can be made up on the spot, depending on your mood and the nature of your interrogator. Feeling too drained today to think up an ICP of your own? Don't fret. It's perfectly acceptable to appropriate your friends' children for effective and instant ICPs. Just be sure you're not talking to *mutual* friends at the time.

ICPs give you the control you crave in your social interactions. Not having children is no obstacle to having children—with the right frame of mind and creative incentive. Remember: Sometimes it's better to have lied and glossed than to have nothing to say at the cocktail party to the boss's boss, when he asks how the kids are doing.

And let's face it: no matter how poor you might be at dramatization, your fake child will come off a whole lot more real than those kids on the "Barney" shows do.

The Last Word In Dealing With Inquiring Minds

Of course, one can always choose to meet such questions in the time-honored way of impressive ladies dating back to Miss Linc and Norma Jean, and currently approved by such sages of modern manners as Auntie Estradiol and Miss Conception, alike: the cold, sustained, silent stare—off into the distance, if one so chooses.

Think of it as a Perpetually Pregnantly Paused Pause. For come what may, even the most rapier sharp inquisitioner can never really read your mind, or any other part of you, no matter how hard she may seem to be trying. Just remember, your husband is trying even harder, and deserves what he's after a whole lot more.

In short, sometimes, the best last word is no word at all. Let the other guy (or gal) scamper to fill the conversational void. We're too evolved to trifle.

Exceptional Conceptions—Answering Words of Wisdom

It's bad enough that Inquiring Minds want to know. Infertile couples must also contend with those who think they know more about infertility than the infertile couple themselves:

Every infertile woman can expect to encounter scads of people offering stories of Exceptional Conceptions. This quick and easy reference guide, offered with your convenience and psychological well-being in mind, will also keep you from throttling unsuspecting people who think they're giving you hope, when you actually feel as if they're giving you a used tissue.

Like nosy questions, well-meaning "words of wisdom" are a constant irritant. If one remains infertile long enough, however, longevity does have its rewards. You will soon discover classic patterns in this behavior, enabling you to quickly respond with one of the suggested actions described below:

Words of Wisdom
"My_____

a)   friend
b)   sister
c)   colleague
d)   neighbor
e)   8th grade algebra teacher
f)   friend's, friend's friend

went through the same thing and got pregnant when she _____

a)   stopped trying so hard
b)   adopted another child
c)   least expected it
d)   started praying to Deepockets Ch-Oprah
e)   was finally able to explain to me how to solve for "x"
f)   stopped being friends with my friend's friend.

Recommended Actions

a)   Leave the room at the tell-tale syllable "M-Y."
b)   Yawn. This may be rude, but sometimes, two wrongs *do* make a right.
c)   Change the subject to something more suitable. Like religion or politics.
d)   Refer to the set of "Get Out Of Fail Free" cards at the end of this book.
e)   Explain that your doctor has assured you that unlike Batman and Bruce Wayne, you and that other individual she describes are not in reality the same person. Hearing about her pregnancy does not necessarily make you feel better. It may, in fact, make you feel worse.
f)   Based on the "six degrees of separation" theory, you *are* your friend's friend's friend. And you can verify that the story she heard is, in fact, not true.

The Trouble With Soothsayers

As annoying as Infertility Witchdoctors and Exceptional Conception stories may be, you will often find their equals among Infertility Soothsayers. These are friends with children who think they really know what it's like to be infertile and who act on that belief—with the full conviction that they are right on target, even when they're about as accurate as an expired home ovulation test kit. Truly tragic.

While every Pregnot woman has her own tolerance levels for such things as being present at kids' birthday parties and the presence of kids in restaurants, one does make exceptions for the children of good friends. Notably, this is usually because what makes friends "good" is their ability to be thoughtful, kind and considerate, without being condescending, presumptuous and preachy.

Infertility Soothsayers, on the other hand, will pull such stunts as kidnapping their own toddlers in restaurant parking lots and careening into the night on two wheels, all based on the assumption that you—pitiable thing—can't handle the sight of their children. They will also refrain from sending you letters— with or without photos of their kids—announcing the imminent arrival of their next child. You see, they know you just can't bear to learn of their good fortune. One can almost hear them tut-tutting your loser status as they pass you over for the annual holiday kiddie portrait.

Do they think they can forever shield you from the products of their procreational prowess? Does this mean they have already determined that you should not be invited to the Bar Mitzvah? Communion? Wedding? And what about grandchildren? Will you be spared the sight of them, as well? Canned Parenthood suggests that by then, the point may well be moot, though this is the one outcome that Soothsayers seem incapable of presaging.

For while these ever conscientious mind-readers carefully censor their lives especially for you—purging from all correspondence or face-to-face encounters any evidence of their children's existence—they are also unwittingly paving the way to the inevitable dissolution of your friendship. Alas, pretty soon, their family will have no contact with you whatsoever. 'Tis a pity, as their children—while they may lack their parents' prescience—are likely not only to have more sense than their parents do, but also to be more interesting than they are.

Still feel the need to keep the lines of communication open in the hope your fecund, former friends will change their tune? Employ the help of mutual friends. Tell them you understand the Soothsayers' good intentions, but that it would be greatly appreciated if you and your spouse were treated like members of the human race in good standing.

Explain that while we the Not Knocked-Up do tend to have our bouts with Fetus-Envy, we're not beneath celebrating the good fortune of those with whom we've established good relationships. It's just that we've discovered that sometimes, it's best to draw the line at the Discovery Zone parking lot.

On the other hand, those of you who have zero-tolerance for Christmas-time newsletters the size of the Sunday *New York Times* and depth of *Highlights* magazine should think long and hard about forsaking your forsaken-ness.

Why Adoption Is Not Always An Option

A beautiful thing
to bring home a child to love.
But just to conceive?

A not-so-gentle rumination on why people should refrain from urging infertile couples to adopt just because "A lot of people conceive a child after adopting."

Removed from the realm of superstition, Infertility Witchdoctor remedies often harbor some rather insidious undertones. Behold:

Typical Infertility Witchdoctor: "You know, a lot of people become pregnant after they adopt." Note that such sentences often end prematurely, stopping at the word "adopt," or "adopting" (as in, "Have you considered adopting?"). What's missing, of course, at the end of these sentences, is that all-important ingredient, the child. This is indicative of the darker nature of such advice. Let's take this infertility "cure" to its logical conclusion:

You may not be ready to adopt a child. And it seems unseemly to do so just to prove or disprove the notion of sympathetic, yet clueless, friends and family who insist that if only you would adopt a child, you would soon conceive another one. Wouldn't it be lovely for an adopted child to learn that your primary motivation for taking him into your life in the first place was the hope that you would soon have another child because of him?

What to do with said adopted child, if after oh, say, five years, this particular lucky charm fails to conjure the desired infant? Send him back to the agency? Give him to another infertile couple, who might have better Karma?

Let's check in with CP's resident Social Worker, Rose Glasses and her clients, Sarah and Abe Lifesabich:

Sarah Lifesabich: "Lucky seems to be a bright, well-adjusted child, and we were glad to give him a home for the past five years. But he just isn't cutting it in terms of helping us to conceive. What do you think we should do?"

Rose Glasses: "Lucky, how do you feel about all of this?"

Lucky Lifesabich: "Well, I don't know. Things have been pretty rough for me right from the start. First of all, I used to spend all my time wishing that I was a girl. I thought if I was a girl, maybe my name would have been 'Lucy,' and I wouldn't have to go through life with a dog's name. But then I found out that if I had been a girl, my parents would have named me "Genie" and decorated my room like the inside of a magic lamp. It's bad enough they're constantly rubbing my head and that disgusting old Diaper Genie. Do you have any idea what a 5-year-old Diaper Genie smells like?"

Rose Glasses: "It sounds like it might not be so difficult for you to leave the Lifesabich home."

Lucky Lifesabich: "Are you kidding? My parents went to a psychic who told them that surrounding themselves with green would bring them their own baby. So everything in my room is green—green carpeting, green walls, green ceiling, green bed linens. When I get sick, nobody even notices. There are plants all over the house and my dad spends hours every day trying to fertilize everything in sight. The lawn looks great. But my mom looks really tired all the time and my dad doesn't even have the strength to play catch with me.

"I lost all my friends, when my parents sold our house in Union to move to Conception. As for food, so much for nutrition. For me, it's nothing but Lucky Charms. Lucky Charms for breakfast, Lucky Charms after school, Lucky Charms before bedtime. Let me tell you, after five years, they're not so magically delicious. Can't I just get an Oreo or a Twinkie once in a while like a normal kid? Heck, even a piece of Oscar Mayer bologna every now and then would be a good break. But I guess they're saving the real kids' food for the real kid.

"And my mother, she's constantly running to the doctor. There are syringes and needles all over the house. When I asked for a new swing set, she gave me mood swings. When I asked for a new video game, she gave me an ultrasound machine. When I asked for a reason why, she said why should she be the only one that's miserable, Goddammit?! My father calls her a Lupron Loony, but I still have to call her 'Mom.' When I tell her it's not fair, she just says, 'You might as well learn right here and now that life's not fair and get used to it, young man.' My dad blames it on stress, but I can't help feeling that it's all my fault."

Rose Glasses: "Mr. Lifesabich, what do you say to all of this?"

Abe Lifesabich: "I just don't know anymore. All I can tell you is that for a woman who keeps saying that above all else, she needs closure, my wife spends an awful lot of time with her feet in stirrups. That doctor sees more of her than I do. No wonder she can't conceive. At this point, I would half expect the baby to *look* like her doctor. Come to think of it, maybe that's who Lucky here resembles . . ."

Rose Glasses: "Lucky, you stay with me. We'll try to find you a more suitable home. I understand Mrs. Lifesabich's neighbor, Myrtle Ovum, has tons of kids and is always happy to welcome one more."

"Mr. and Mrs. Lifesabich, this is obviously not working out for you. Have you tried prenatal vitamins, valerian root, baby aspirin, changing doctors, standing on your head after sex, standing on your head during sex, exercising, not exercising, praying, having sex on Friday nights, trying a doctor in New York, trying a doctor in Colorado, increasing your medication doses and wearing boxer shorts?

"Good. Very good. Keep up the good work. Stay optimistic. Keep communicating with each other. Keep up on the latest research. Get to the pharmacy on time. Make sure your health insurance is up to date. Don't miss any doctor's appointments, even on the weekends. Make sure you've had all the necessary tests. Try not to miss too much work; you need to save up those parental leave days, just in case. And above all, don't forget to relax. That's very important."

Managing The Mother Of Them All: Mother's Day

The man in the store
gives flowers to each woman.
Will he want mine back?

Getting through the most difficult day of the year:

Every Mother's Day, thousands of infertile women are reduced to an emotional status akin to High School Senior Without A Prom Date. This is hardly nostalgic. Nor does it become more so after the age of 35. Quite the contrary. Being a Non-Mom on Mother's Day is similar to being Jewish on Christmas, except that the feeling lasts all year: While everyone else is celebrating, you spend the day hoping that something more fulfilling than a visit to a Chinese restaurant will come along to fill the void.

Thanks to CP, it has. Next Mother's Day, why not join us for the Million Non-Mom March, when we'll converge on Washington chanting such motivational and empowering slogans as:

- The Whole World Is Watching (as we try to procreate)
- Power To The Pregnantly Paused People
- Remember The McCon Seven
- Where's The Beef? (especially meaningful for those undergoing intra-uterine-insemination and invitro-fertilization techniques)
- Support *Civil* Disobedience. Ban Lupron.
- We're Mad As Hell And We're Not Gonna Take It Anymore! (until a new treatment becomes available)
- Practice Safe Sex: Do It In The Lab
- Adopt This: Mind Your Own Business!
- We Demand Equal Treatment: Give Us Some Damn Flowers
- Infertility Is Not Healthy For Embryos And Other Living Things
- This Is Your Ovary. This Is Your Ovary On Pergonal
- We Bear No Heirs. Get Used To It.
- Always Menstruation, Despite Relaxation
- We Make Love, Not Babies

and finally,

- We're One Million Strong. And We're Gonna Stay That

Way.

Join us for this unparalleled opportunity to bond with your sisters in fertility futility while fighting to raise awareness of our plight.

CHAPTER SEVEN

What's Up Doc?
(Besides My Patience and My Feet?!)

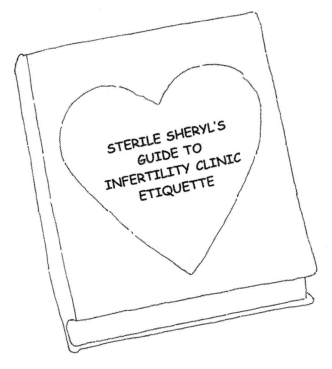

STERILE SHERYL'S
GUIDE TO
INFERTILITY CLINIC
ETIQUETTE

Infertility Clinic Etiquette

Another cycle
filled with hope, optimism.
Ultrasounds abound.

Routine Ob-Gyn visits are bad enough. But infertility has established a whole new benchmark for discomfort in the doctor's office. Some typical experiences are addressed by CP's resident (and very patient) patient coordinator, Sterile Sheryl:

Dis-dressed Impatient: I'm not comfortable with the transvaginal ultrasound procedure, yet I know it's a crucial part of my diagnosis and treatment. Can CP help me feel better about this?

Sterile Sheryl: Yes. You can expect a small diamond ring from your ultrasound technician on your third visit.

Dis-dressed Impatient: My ultrasound technician occasionally misguides the scanner toward my butt (inadvertently, I'm sure). How can I politely correct her?

Sterile Sheryl: CP assures you that this is, indeed, inadvertent. Those examination rooms are *dark*. Here are some ways to address the problem:

- Gently take hold of the wand and guide it where it belongs, saying something like, "Here, let me help."
- Suggest a nearby medical school with a good Proctology program.
- Tell her if she doesn't cut it out, you'll send her to Dr. Ruth for anatomy lessons.
- Squeal like a pig.

Dis-dressed Impatient: Is it okay to compare notes with other women in the doctor's waiting room, who I know are going through the same ordeal?

Sterile Sheryl: It's acceptable, as long as you're prepared for the eventuality that they may become pregnant and you may not. It's sort of like buying lottery tickets at the same time and place as your friends and finding out that everyone but you hit the jackpot. Your consolation prize: You may come into some fertility drug left-overs.

Dis-dressed Impatient: Is it OK to pee on the toilet seat when relieving my bladder after an extensive ultrasound procedure?

Sterile Sheryl: It's never OK to pee on the toilet seat, regardless of the circumstances. It's bad enough that we in the Not Knocked-Up sisterhood are frequently pooped upon by fate. It's up to each of us to see that we don't in turn pee upon each other. Leaving behind a clean toilet seat is the one true measure of civility. No real lady leaves traces of her behind— behind.

Dis-dressed Impatient: When should my husband accompany me to the infertility clinic?

Sterile Sheryl: There are times when he *must* accompany you to the clinic. These are the days when he's needed to produce a specimen and/or drive you home after a procedure requiring anesthesia, or one that is otherwise so physically and emotionally draining that you simply can't go it alone. In reality, though, most husbands can't make it to a scintilla of office visits required for a typical IUI or IVF cycle.

Logistics aside, it makes sense to *schlep* your hubby to a minimum of one gratuitous office visit per cycle, just to ensure that he knows firsthand—at least to some extent—what it is you're dealing with. For this same reason, it's advisable to take your "meds" in his presence as often as possible and sometimes involve him in the process directly. That way, if you actually do have a successful pregnancy, you can feel secure in the knowledge that you were in the same room at the same time during some crucial moments in the process.

Dis-dressed Impatient: My husband would prefer to produce a specimen at the doctor's office, rather than at home. Is this permissible?

Sterile Sheryl: Many men forsake the privacy of bringing a semen specimen from home for the security of knowing their specimen will not wind up all over their leather car seats or too late to be usable. The thoughtful Pregnantly Paused wife will buy him his own issues of *Playboy* and *Penthouse,* so he'll have "fresh meat" with which to work when he arrives at the clinic. Too embarrassed to go this route? Think about this: If you feel you've yawned through every tired old magazine in the doctor's waiting room, just imagine how he must feel having to share those hand-job hand-me-downs when it's time to deliver a specimen.

Dress for Success (Or At Least Less Mess)

Infertile women
always have well groomed feet, toes.
Long time in stirrups.

The down and not-so-dirty ins and outs of getting in and out of the infertility clinic quickly, if not painlessly:

You may not find that *ultimate* success as you head down the road to hoped-for fertility. But this toe-to-head guide to dressing for success for those interminable visits to the infertility clinic will get you wherever it is you might end up in (relatively) hassle-free style. Follow CP's time-tested time-savers; at least you won't be fighting with your own clothes, along with everything else. Isn't your life complicated enough already?

Suggested Wear

Ease into your barrage of Pregnantly Paused appointments with these simple appointments:

- Slip-on shoes
- Knee highs
- Clean, pristine panties
- Slacks
- Short-sleeved tops with a jacket *or*
- loose long-sleeved blouses (For easy to access, easy to hide blood test sites)
- Short or loose hair

Wear and Tear

Avoid these time and energy wasters:

- Complex shoes (those with buckles, laces, claps, etc.)
- Pantyhose
- Long shirts and tunics
- Shirts with tight sleeves
- Complicated hairdos, hairclips and hairbands (Your hair comes undone, while the ubiquitous ultrasound exam becomes ultimately more uncomfortable and unclear.)

Don't Go There!

Finally found a reputable specialist? Don't turn him off with a faux pas:

- Anything other than clean panties and feet
  (Yeah, we know the medical team deals with this stuff all the time. But do you really want them to suddenly remember to review your particular case as they commence their Filet 'O Fish Sandwich lunch?)

Other Fare

Like any other experienced traveler, the experienced Pregnot woman will always be appropriately equipped for her journey, come what may:

- A good book
- A concise list of billing and insurance questions
- A cell phone
- Sunglasses (when being infertile also requires being incognito)
- The *cojones* to leave the waiting room when talk among pregnant patients awaiting ultrasound exams turns to the delivery room

The Real Meanings Behind Common Infertility Terms and Phrases

So many new words.
So many new positions.
So few with husband.

Infertile women learn a whole new lexicon concerning the condition, its causes and treatments. Here are some brief definitions of common terms associated with infertility, and CP's alternative translations, which more accurately reflect the ordeal:

Adoption—Often cited as an easy remedy for infertility—usually by those who already have a swarm of children of their own, whose names they may or may not be able to remember, and who may or may not adhere to prescribed bedtimes or any other form of traditional disciplinary measures. The first thing we, the Perpetually Pregnantly Paused, truly must adopt, therefore, is the attitude that we, and only we, can know what is right for our families, no matter how small they might be when all is said and done. Is adoption an option for you?

91

Perhaps. Perhaps, even, a remarkable one. But that's your decision to make in your own good time—and no one else's.

ART—An acronym for "Assisted Reproductive Technologies." Don't be misled by the cutesy allusion to high culture. There is little aesthetic pleasure to be found in procuring and administering fertility medications, sperm counts, transvaginal ultrasound procedures, egg retrievals and the like. These experiences have little to do with art, far more to do with science and—we at CP suspect—much to do with alchemy. But certain cubist-era depictions of women do come close to portraying the effects of infertility on one's psyche.

Canned Pregnancy—Come to us when you're feeling blue, or any of the following sensations: hot flashes, violent impulses, the uncontrollable desire to pee on a stick, the unrelenting urge to cry, a Lupron overdose (or a normal dose, depending on your husband's ability to cope), or worse. Call toll-free 1-800-UA-BITCH anywhere in the U.S.

Cycling—Often used to describe a month during which a woman endures an IUI or IVF cycle. Ironically reminiscent of riding a stationary bicycle, as you may often participate in a great deal of wheel spinning without enjoying any forward progress.

Egg Retrieval—The point in an IVF cycle at which your doctor will remove multiple eggs from your ovaries in order to place them in a petri dish with your husband's sperm. At this crucial stage of your cycle, it's best not to have a doctor that reminds you of Frank Purdue.

Endometriosis—A condition associated with infertility in which menstrual fluids are believed to back up in a woman's body, rather than flowing out. Aptly named, as the "end" at the beginning of the word can presage the end of the line for would-be mothers. (Often confused with "supercalifragilisticexbealidotious," of Mary Poppins fame, but a different kind of nonsense song, altogether.)

E-2 Level—Refers to estradiol, a hormone produced by the ovaries during a cycle. Your E-2, or estradiol level, is one of many clues your doctor will use to determine the progress of your *IUI* or *IVF* cycle (see definitions below). When your hormones are a-hummin' your E-2 will be a-soarin'. The experienced Not Knocked-Up woman can usually approximate her own E-2 level by calculating the degree to which she "feels pretty" (nay, even horny), in spite of the *Lupron* injections she started several days earlier (see below).

Family Friendly—Perpetually Pregnantly Paused Prohibitive.

Frozen Embryo Transfer (FET)—Some women are fortunate enough to come away from an *IVF* cycle with two or more viable embryos that can be frozen for a later, additional attempt at conception. The beauty of this system is that it provides an extra glimmer of hope to infertile couples. The difficulty of this system is that it provides an extra glimmer of hope to infertile couples. Hop on the roller coaster for one more (certainly not free) ride. Conveniently, FET also stands for *Forever Eager Tenacity*.

Fibroids—Usually benign, yet problematic growths in and around the uterus that may impede pregnancy. The good news: Fibroids are usually benign and can often be removed. The bad news: It may not help. The great equalizer: Not Knocked-Up women contending with the glitch of fibroids may take some comfort in knowing that many pregnant women must contend with the itch of hemorrhoids. Ain't life a bitch?

Hyperstimulation—This occurs when your body responds to fertility treatments by producing so many eggs that one or both ovaries become enlarged, often causing painful abdominal swelling. Your doctor may ask you to curtail physical activity, and in severe cases, even place you on bed rest. The good news is that if your eggs are healthy, you may have a better than average chance of conception during that cycle. The bad news is twofold: In all likelihood, your doctor will also want you to abstain from having sex. And if you ovulate, you'll feel like a gang of college kids on spring break are playing a game of beach volleyball in your uterus.

IUI—Conventionally, intra-uterine insemination, in which fertility drugs are used to increase egg production, ovulation is chemically stimulated and specially treated sperm are placed into the cervix at a scientifically designated time to increase the chance of fertilization. In actuality, IUI stands for "Introductory Ulcer Inducer," as it is often a mere precursor to the more complex, expensive and stressful *IVF* procedure (see below).

IVF—In commonly accepted parlance, this refers to invitro-fertilization, the process by which a woman's eggs are fertilized (one hopes) outside of her body. In common usage, however, IVF stands for "I'm Very Finished," as we all know that the treatment yields but a 20-25 percent chance of full-term pregnancy, while costing approximately $10,000 a shot (twice a day, no less).

Lupron—A medication administered through subcutaneous injection that produces a temporary state of menopause in preparation for an IVF cycle. Doctors employ Lupron so they can manipulate your body's hormone production, without interference from—your body. Side effects: May turn normal, healthy, infertile women into homicidal shrews. They say that Robert Louis Stevenson literally dreamed up Dr. Jekyll and Mr. Hyde during a nightmare. Lupron is truly the author's dream come true. CP staff is certain that we will see a murder case in our lifetime in which the defense is "insanity by Lupron." To illustrate: If Nicole Brown was on Lupron the night of her murder, she would still be alive today. O.J. would not.

Meds—Short for "medications," which are used to induce *Super-Ovulation* (see definition below). One of the joys of infertility is getting to know how to prepare your own "meds" and give yourself injections—right in the privacy of your own home! Infertility gives you the chance to learn your A, B, CC's. You're not a doctor; but you play one—sort of. It would be helpful to be paid like one, since investing in "meds" can set you back thousands of dollars a cycle.

Menses—The indomitable, invincible, interminable, menstrual flow. Related words:
Mega-Menses—A particularly heavy menstrual flow
Meta-Menses—The discipline of studying and discussing the menstrual flow (like this!)
    and
Mensa-Menses—Super-advanced menstruation techniques for those who have become Pregnantly Paused at the genius level.

The Other Woman—Any woman who is pregnant.

Polycystic Ovary Syndrome—This condition, formally identified in the 1930s, is frequently associated with infertility. Characterized by large, cystic ovaries, excess facial and body hair and irregular menstrual periods, the syndrome can be overcome with hormone treatment, but not necessarily before its sufferers become overwrought with stress. Nonetheless, if you can pronounce it, you can denounce it. And if you can denounce it, chances are you can beat it like an infertile husband on ovulation day. We at Canned Parenthood know several women diagnosed with this condition who are now happy, if harried, mothers.

Post-Coital Test—Your doctor determines through a microscopic sample how your partner's sperm reacts to your bodily fluids immediately after sex. For many, this experience is the entry-level carnival ride in the great un-amusing, disillusionment park that so often crescendos with the infamous infertility roller coaster. The good news: This test actually follows a real sexual encounter. The bad news: If you're a hard-core infertility case, subsequent efforts to conceive may bear more resemblance to alien abduction stories than to love stories. Also, note that sperm found through post-coital testing to be swimming the wrong way will *never* stop to ask for directions—just like Daddy.

Prenatal Vitamins—With lots of folic acid to prevent serious birth defects, they say these are really good to take when you're expecting or trying to be. For all we know, you might as well take expectorant if you've been infertile for so long that you can't conceive of going back to good, old-fashioned One-A-Days in the next 365.

Scan—Infertility clinic lingo for *transvaginal ultrasound* (see below entry—no pun intended). Don't be fooled. When they say they're going to "scan" you, they don't mean they're sending you through one of those devices you see at the airport security check point, although at times, you will feel like a piece of lost luggage going around and around on one of those electronic conveyer belts. It's more like—um—see *transvaginal ultrasound* description for a more detailed account.

Super-Ovulation—Process by which the ovaries are stimulated to produce multiple eggs in a cycle in preparation for an *IVF* or *IUI* attempt. When it works, Super-O can have you cooking up more eggs than "Denny's" at a Sunday brunch. When it doesn't, you'll feel like your emotions have been scrambled up by a Cuisinart. These costly and painful drugs can turn you into a werewolfette. But emergency trips to the far-off pharmacy for that far-out pharmaceutical can have some exciting fringe benefits. A year into my chemical dependency on infertility drugs, I noticed that my breasts—with no surgical enhancement—grew a full cup size. Surely, this is God's way of saying, "Sorry about the infertility. Keep the boobs."

Transvaginal Ultrasound—What it is: A remarkable technology that enables physicians and nurses to non-surgically view parts of a woman's reproductive system with great clarity and accuracy. What it feels like: You're a Mustang with a manual five-speed transmission and a newly licensed 17-year-old behind the wheel and on the clutch.

The *Pink* (Is For Girls) *Panther:* Covert Operations—Secret Rites And Rituals Of The Pregnantly Paused

Sometimes it feels like
the whole doctor's office is
in our bed, watching.

Every infertile woman engages in certain Covert Operations in getting through a cycle. Follow the adventures of Inspector Curlicue Pubeau, as she attempts to unravel the mysteries of Pregnantly Paused Survival:

Once upon a month, our heroine had the bright and kind-hearted notion that she would help her husband through his part of the infertility ordeal by buying him his own "Girlie" magazines with which to "do his thing," when the time came to—um, cum:

Inspector Pubeau left work early and headed for a small gas station-24 hour convenience store, reasoning that a) she'd beat the rush hour crowd; b) she never goes in there otherwise, and c) no one else will bear witness to her purchase, because the store is so very small and easily "cased." Too bad, they don't carry such disgusting merchandise here, the clerk informs her. She left, noticing that his leer could probably get him arrested in several states.

Next stop—a slightly larger convenience store. Only one customer ahead of her on line. Good. This is exactly the kind of convenience Pubeau was hoping for. A woman behind the counter. More convenient yet. But what's this? By the time she's face to face with the cashier, a veritable army of construction workers lines up behind her—to buy "Girlie" magazines. Uh, never mind.

Stop three: the giant, local bookstore chain—café lattes, calendars of every stripe for every fad and hobby, "New In Non-Fiction," *New York Times* Best Sellers. Trend-ily speaking, the place to see and be seen. But not today. This Covert Operation demands an impossible degree of privacy. Still, this is our Not Knocked-Up sister's only remaining venue for obtaining a four-color, two-dimensional, sure-fire love connection before tomorrow morning's date with embryonic destiny. And so she perseveres. For him. For their future. For their family. (Maybe.)

Now—the "Information" counter is hallowed ground in this bastion of fine literature and intellectual stimulation. Here, Pubeau will find the hard-to-locate, newly available in paperback tome her mother has been yearning for. Here, she will inquire as to the release date of her favorite author's latest belles lettres. Here, she will exchange knowing glances with the store clerk about "I Was Amelia Earhardt," when the gentleman in front of her inquires about it. Here, she seeks out first editions of the latest Ann Tyler and Amy Tan novels. Here, she will ask if they carry *Playboy* and *Penthouse*—just as soon as everyone else in line is not only gone, but also dead.

Once the question is posed, the ever helpful saleswoman will inform her that, yes, they do carry those publications. Which one does she want?

Neither, thinks our Perpetually Pregnantly Paused friend. "Both," she answers, anyway.

Playboy and *Penthouse* appear from beneath the "Information" counter like horny rabbits coming out of a hot hat. In heat-sealed, see-through, plastic wrap, no less.

"Can I pay for these here?" our heroine inquires in desperation.

But alas, there is no cash register at the "Information" desk, only—well—information. And, of course, pornography.

And so Pubeau must trudge across the entire, jumbo, café latte, book, cat calendar, dog calendar, *Partridge Family* calendar, *Dilbert* calendar, social calendar store, where everyone's encouraged to just hang around and browse and check out all the merchandise and all the other patrons all they please. Proceeding unnoticed to the promised land of cash registers, brown paper bags and ultimate anonymity is a challenge befitting our Not Knocked-Up Inspector. Who else could shoulder such potential humiliation with such *cojones*? You think this will intimidate our Pubeau, after all she's been through? Hah! This woman has endured countless transvaginal ultrasound scans and needle sticks; she can describe myriad stirrup styles in minute detail and recount with the precision of a supersonic microscope the balding pattern of her doctor's scalp.

At last, arriving at the check-out line, our heroine passes the time by chanting this silent mantra, as those behind her strain to steal peeks at her purchases:

> *Iswearthisstuffisn'tformeifonlyyouknewwhy
> Iwasbuyingthisyouwouldn'tlookatmelikeIwassome
> kindofweirdoI'mreallyaverynicedecentpersonjusttryingto
> helpmyhusbandandstartafamilyofourownsurely
> youcanunderstandthat...*over and over again.

And this is somehow the subliminal cue for the guy at the cash register to wave her copies of *Playboy* and *Penthouse* in the air for all the store and all the world to see and ask boldly—After all, *What does he care?*—"Hey, how much do these things cost?!"

as renowned figure skater Kitty-Kat Twit—naked!—and some nameless lesbian body painters flail around on glossy cover shots for all the store and all the world to see.

But Pubeau remains calm. There's always the mantra. And it will all be worth it when she arrives home and gives her husband the gift that will keep on giving out. And all for the noble cause of the chance to create a new life together—even if they aren't exactly together when that happens.

"Oh!" the Inspector's husband exclaims, when Pubeau bestows upon him the fruits of her selfless and heroic travails. "I could *never* bring this stuff to the doctor's office. I'd be way too embarrassed."

CHAPTER EIGHT

A New Take On The Boob Tube For
Those Without Breast Pumps

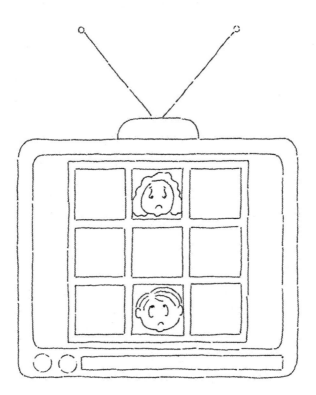

I Want My CPTV: The Not Knocked-Up All The Time Channel

Who will take care of
me in my dotage? A son?
Daughter? Dog? TV.

A TV Guide For The IVF Crowd:

T urn on, tune in and drop your pants . . . for that ovulation inducing injection! We want our CPTV—Canned Pregnancy's Own Premium Cable Channel. Join us for the ultimate Not Knocked-Up viewing experience 24-hours-a-day. Check out these old favorites with renewed appreciation. All programs are rated Y-ME:

The Bob Newhart Show—Bob and Emily: No kids, no questions, no sweat.

Cops—Those perps were born to *someone*. Not us! Phew! You have the right to remain infertile . . .

Gilligan's Island—Seven adults, no kids, no escape. Kind of like the infertility clinic waiting room early on a Sunday morning. In addition, each episode features a glimmer of hope for rescue. But at the end, the castaways are once again stranded indefinitely. Boy, can we relate. Coconut cream pie, anyone?

The Honeymooners—Alice and Ralph don't have much, including kids. Come to think of it, neither do upstairs neighbors Trixie and Ed Norton. But they do have each other. Could they

103

still be "Honeymooners" if they had kids? No way. And for that—Baby, they're the greatest. (We also suspect that, though childless, the Kramdens did spawn later-run TV duos like Bob and Emily and Dick and Joanna.)

Jeopardy!—No tiny tots. And Double Jeopardy has nothing whatsoever to do with twins. Meanwhile, the intellectual stimulation will take your mind off your hyperstimulation woes. And just imagine how well we would do if the show ever unveils a category of infertility clues. It would be worth the wait just to hear the following exchange:

> Contestant: "I'll take polycystic ovary syndrome Before & After for 1,000, please, Alex."
> Alex: "The answer is, 'Hic! Gimme another fuzzy navel.'"
> Contestant: "What is drinking to excess body hair?"
> What're the odds?

The Jerry Springer Show—Just a half-hour of this stuff will make you feel pretty good about not contributing any more humans to the species.

Judge Judy—Finally, a woman in complete control of her environment. Dispensing justice. Setting things right. We need more of this in real life.

The Mary Tyler Moore Show—Who can turn the world on without child? Mary and Rhoda spend so much time working and worrying about being single, that they never even broach the topic of parenthood. Bless them. Meanwhile, obnoxious, self-absorbed, stay-at-home mom Phyllis is fodder for lots of running gags. CPTV's heartiest thanks to MTM. We know we'll make it after all.

M*A*S*H—Lots of blood, fighting and doctors. Not many kids. And yet, they laugh.

The Mickey Mouse Club—Continuous reruns of "Anything Can Happen Day" episodes remind us that anything *can* happen. Sometimes, even good things, depending on the month.

My Three Sons—Back in the '60s, single father Steve Douglas, irascible Uncle Charlie and three sons set up housekeeping as one of TV's very first unconventional, and therefore, un-nuclear, sitcom families. Not only is there no pearl-clad mom in the picture, but youngest son Ernie is also adopted. Big brother Robby and wife Katy have triplets, while no drugs—fertility, hallucinatory or other, like ya know, junky stuff—are involved. Ah, such sweet '60s innocence! It'll cream ya.

Newhart—Dick and Joanna: No kids, no questions, no sweat. We knew Newhart's humor was dry; now we know his TV alter-egos are dry, too, in their own prime-time way. And we love them for it.

Richard Simmons Infomercials—Sweatin' to the Oldies, featuring women, many of whom gained tons of weight during their pregnancies.

Note: Some shows that would not normally be considered acceptable fare for our Pregnantly Paused viewing audience, due to their nauseating idolatry of the nuclear family, may be added to the CPTV schedule from time to time. Vintage programs, dating back to the late 1950s and early 1960s, can earn acceptance by CPTV censors if they feature scenes in which husbands and wives (who are also invariably Dads and Moms) are shown sleeping in separate beds.

Here, the Not Knocked-Up viewer can take comfort in the following: It's readily apparent that conception could not have been an easy task in such cases. And extra-conceptual sexual shenanigans could hardly have been too spontaneous either.

Don't Miss Our Own Custom Programming

CPTV Movie Classics—Tune in for such Not Knocked-Up-friendly fare as

- "Raising Arizona," in which Nicholas Cage and Holly Hunter play an infertile couple who try to even the score by kidnapping one of a millionaire's sextuplets. (Do as they say, not as they portray. CP does not—repeat—does not advocate illegal activities. We do not want you to go to jail. This is supposed to be fiction; just because you can't get pregnant doesn't mean you might prefer a broom stick to your husband's dick.)

- "Beetlejuice," in which the previously childless Maitlands, played by Alec Baldwin and Geena Davis, fill their Connecticut country home with the pitter-patter of Winona Ryder's little feet—after perishing in a car accident and haunting their own house. Watch for Davis' priceless look of courteous disdain early in the flick, when a pesty realtor tells her that their large home would really be more suitable for a couple with a family. It's a cinematic moment of rare infertility cinema verite and Not Knocked-Up empathy.

And don't miss our repeat screenings of

- "Rosemary's Baby." What better reminder that pregnancy and childbirth aren't necessarily all they're cracked up to be? Poor Mia Farrow. Bad hair, bad husband, bad neighbors, and alas, bad seed. Is it any wonder she later switched to adopting her children?

A Made for CPTV Movie Classic—"E-2: The Extra-Ovulator:" In this slam-bang—yet extremely moving—G-rated tear-jerker, an alien being from planet Ov-R-35 fails to conceive without high-tech ovarian stimulation meds. Left alone and stranded in a strange suburban nuclear family world by her pregnant contemporaries, she is finally adopted by a sensitive 9-year-old, the son of a divorced, single mom. Together, they make for a happy, albeit unconventional family unit—until E-2 becomes lonely for her husband, old friends and infertility clinic.

E-2: Don't phone home. Phone your doctor, instead, for your latest estradiol level. Your friendly nurse coordinator will explain the universe to you (at least as it stands for the next 24 hours). Need more follicles? Just click your heels together three times and repeat: There's nothing like hormones, there's nothing like hormones, there's nothing like hormones. Chances are, there's an injection out there just waiting to bring you right back down to earth.

CPTVNews—Every serious cable channel needs its own news show. This is a particularly important aspect of CPTV's programming strategy. Watching at least a half-hour of serious news about world and national events will put your personal problems into perspective and have you counting your blessings along with your E-2 levels, follicles and cycle days.

What You Won't See On CPTV

Our broadcasts will strictly omit coverage of events such as the much ballyhooed births and birthdays of the McCon septuplets. CPTV is a McCon-free, stress-free viewing zone. CP takes the position (no pun intended) with which many, if not most, Not Knocked-Up women would agree: When it comes to infertility, the McCons—who took fertility drugs, conceived a batch of babies and—against doctors' orders—carried them all to term—are just not the real McCoy. This is simply not the model on which to model our goals in seeking family harmony. For further explanation, here's a word from our resident media analyst, Sonny Synic:

> *We at CPTVNews wish the McCons well—all 10 of them. (Let's not forget, before the Iowa 7 hit town, the McCons already had a daughter.) But watching the McCons cavort with their brood is like watching someone win the Showcase Showdown on The Price Is Right—someone who was obviously chosen as a contestant because she wasn't wearing a bra, and the producers wanted to see her run down the aisle to take her place on "Contestants Row." Sure, it's nice to see someone win, but should we really be rewarding that kind of behavior? I think not.*
>
> *That's the Sonny-side view for today. Have a good one, and I hope you're ovulating! This is Sonny Synic signing off.*

CHAPTER NINE

The Green, Green Frog and The Blue, Blue Browns, And Other Tales To Soothe The Pregnantly Paused Soul

Duo-Disney—Where The World Walks Only In Pairs

Ride with us, baby.
We go in one direction:
Wherever you want.

Infertile couples can find solace and companionship—but not pregnant women with kids—at this utopian theme park designed just for them:

P regnant women wouldn't be so bad, if only they were contagious. And stay-at-home moms wouldn't be so bad, if only they would *Stay At Home!* But alas, they rarely do. Uh-uh. There they are in TGI Fridays, failing to discipline their kids, or in the mall, pushing their strollers around like miniature, territorial tanks.

You've heard of—perhaps even been to—Disneyland, Disney World or Euro-Disney. Now, it's time for Duo-Disney. Yes, Duo-Disney, a theme park—Nay!—an entire microcosm of society, devoted solely to making life fun and interesting for couples without children.

You won't find any lines at Duo-Disney; resort management (aka Canned Parenthood) knows all too well that you and your hubby have already done way more than your fair share of waiting. No roller coaster rides, either. We figure you're up to here with ups and downs as it is. And you'll hear nary a strain of "It's a Small World After All." After all, we know your heads are already full of annoying stuff you just can't shake.

These are just some of the many thoughtful ways in which we strive to make your stay with us as pleasant as it can be for you and your very intimate family of two. So hop on the Duo-

Rail and get ready for a bump-free, bummer-free ride to our feature attractions:

- No-Pressure Island—A very special haven where no one has children—or will ever ask you why you don't. Dine in a quiet, romantic bistro, surrounded only by a cozy fireplace and other adults. Enjoy a relaxing day at our fine, secluded beach, where you can actually read a book without being interrupted by the piercing sound of shrieking midgets. Take a dip in the pool—without worrying about swimming through gross warm spots of questionable origin. Nap in the quietude of your hotel bed, resting assured that no kids will be running up and down the hallway screaming.

- Teenage Mutant Miscreant Kingdom—A truly terrifying adventure ride in which Duo Disney guests travel through a jungle inhabited by throngs of thong-wearing, tattooed, nipple-ringed youngsters with bad hair dyes and worse attitudes. (Do not fear; they won't speak to anyone over the age of 19.)

- Nuclear (Family) World—one of our most popular attractions, in which Duo Disney guests can drive rented Dodge Minivans around a circular track decorated with scenic soccer fields, mock elementary schools and Chuck-E Cheese restaurants. Frustrated moms-in-waiting are issued "Baby Think It Over" dolls to simulate parenthood. For a slight additional charge, you can video tape your Nuclear (Family) World experiences. For maximum enjoyment, play the tape back when you return to the "real world"—at high volume, in an exclusive restaurant on a Saturday night, when some cretin's brats are rolling around on the floor beneath your table.

- Everyone Is Pregnant Day—You can "be expecting" a great time every Halloween, by simulating the experience of really "expecting." Pregnantly Paused couples can get out of the house to avoid the onslaught of tiny little neighborhood candy moochers and at the same time, have a chance to dress up themselves. Free fanny packs in various sizes are issued to female guests, who are encouraged to strap them around their waists to simulate that most blessed—and elusive—of conditions. Then, rent the maternity outfit of your dreams to cover your very own "Magic Mountain." Ride the amazing infertility roller coaster—guaranteed to simulate the sensation of morning sickness. "Dads" get to play along too, by pampering their "expectant" spouses as they sample the joys of doting, gloating and bloating forbidden them the other 364 days of the year.

- Hall of Unknown Names—The longer it takes to bear a child, the more you will meet people in the interim whom you cannot bear, who bear names you had reserved for your missing little bundle of joy—or, for that matter, people who have usurped your dream name for their pet hamster. Visit the Hall of Unknown Names for a fresh batch of baby names that will not remind you of the office snake who always tries to steal credit for your accomplishments, the guy across the street who mows his lawn at 7 every Saturday morning or your boss's wife.

- Space Molehill—We know you need your space. And we're here to give it to you. Simulate zero-gravity in peace and serenity, while watching your earthbound problems shrink like a guy in a cold meteor shower. Here in Duo-Disney's stratosphere, those monstrous maternity mountains are just zit-sized molehills. Pop 'em!

- Sexpot Center—The ultimate attraction for mutual attraction. Spontaneity is key, so we don't want to flesh things out too much, so to speak. Suffice to say we've recreated such nostalgic nooky nooks as the backseat of an old Buick parked at Look-Out Lane and a seedy (no semen pun intended) No-Tell Motel room to harken back to the days when getting laid was just good, dirty fun. Can't populate? Epcop-ulate to your heart's content with unlimited Viagra and estrogen and rediscover sex for its own sloppy sake. Shed some worries, clothes and years. Make like a Nike commercial and just do it 'til the cows go mad. Get in the Mooooooood for love and stay there!

- It's a Whole World After All—Travel through our tunnel of love, a romantic canal, in your own private gondola (each one seats only two!) amidst the sights and sounds of Venice, Rome, Paris and all points richly beautiful. View an amazing replica of the Taj Mahal, that eternal tribute to romantic love. At journey's end, experience life through the eyes of others who don't fit the nuclear family mold: Special interactive characters representing gay couples and mature singles will remind you that though you may be Not Knocked-Up, you are not alone in the nuclear family world we all inhabit.

Hankering for a souvenir memento of your whimsical trip? No mouse ears for our guests. We figure you're plenty tired of playing lab rat and don't wish for any reminders of the bizarre experiments you've recently endured out in the nuclear family world. Instead, take home a pair of giant-sized human ears. No, they're not real; actually, your ever-industrious hosts have made them out of foam from worn-out mattresses in Sexpot Center: just a token of your Duo-Disney visit—and a reminder to the Witchdoctors you may encounter outside our hallowed gates that they should, from time to time, shut up and listen. Two free pair per pair. Why? Because we like you.

The Hormone Zone

Infertility
is weird enough without Rod
Serling showing up.

The plight of infertility gets a classically eerie TV treatment:

An Infertility Teleplay

Picture if you will a woman who wants desperately to achieve a life-long goal. But there's a funny thing about this goal: She didn't know it was a life-long goal until she couldn't reach it. The more doors she knocked on, the closer she came to nothingness. With each worthless stride, the probability that she would fail was slammed in her face, landing her finally and desperately at our destination today—and hers. Look! At the sign-post up ahead—it's the next stop—the Hormone Zone!

Music Up . . .
Hospital Interior . . .

A woman lies on a hospital gurney, swathed in cool, white sheets. A doctor hovers at the edge of her bed. A group of nurses huddle together in the hazy background.

The surgeon leans toward her:

"Are you ready?" he asks.

"Doctor," she replies, "Tell me the truth. What are the odds that this will work?"

The surgeon hesitates, measuring his response.

"You know—we all know—this is your last chance," he says, finally.

"What if nothing happens?" she asks.

"Let's not think about that right now. Think positive

thoughts. And relax."

But she could not relax. So much was riding on this procedure. If it failed, she knew she would never fit in, doomed to a life of solitude and alienation.

The nurses in the distance spoke in hushed tones among themselves. Occasionally, one of them looked her way.

"Poor thing," said a short plump nurse. "She's been through so much. How many procedures is it now?"

"This will be the fifth—and final—one," replied a second chubby nurse, as she took a drag from her cigarette. "Her chances aren't very good."

"I wouldn't want to be in her shoes," offered another pudgy colleague. "Not for anything."

. . . Fade To Black . . .
. . . Fade In On . . .

An orderly, his movements belabored, emerges from the shadows wheeling the patient from surgery into a recovery room. Hours pass as the effects of the anesthesia wane. Finally, the doctor reappears over the woman's bed. His team of nurses can again be heard murmuring faintly in the hallway. The doctor leans toward his patient.

"Ready?" he asks, as she emerges from a deep sleep, wrapped in a tight cocoon of linens, which obscures the contours of her body and renders her form almost shapeless.

"I dreamed I was pushing a baby in a carriage," she tells him. "Maybe that's an omen."

"Maybe," he replies somberly, not wanting to get her hopes up, nor dash them altogether.

"Are we ready?" he asks again, gently, patiently, resting a hand softly on her shoulder.

"Yes," she whispers.

Her husband joins them at her bedside.

"How did it go, Doc?" he asks.

"We're about to find out."

Slowly, cautiously, the doctor removes the sheets, layer by layer.

She feels her body lightening as the weight of the sheets is lifted from her. She feels as if she's shrinking, losing some essential part of herself, diminishing in some horrible, unnatural way. Long minutes pass as the doctor toils above her.

Finally, he steps away from the bed.

A speculum drops from his hand, clanging against the stained linoleum floor and echoing through the hospital's dank corridor.

"No change!" he yells, defeated. "No change at all!"

The woman leaps from the bed and runs to the full-length mirror hung on the back of the bathroom door. No. There is no change. She remains Perpetually Pregnantly Paused.

The nurses crowd around the door to stop her from escaping to a dangerous destiny. They fear that perhaps, in a moment of utter insanity, she might even head for the maternity ward.

Their swollen bellies protruding like malevolent balloons in a little girl's bad dream, the nurses advance toward her. The surgeon fans his arms like a mother bird protecting its young, as he steps in front of the nurses to bolster their blockade. His breasts heave with the weight of mother's milk. His stomach sways with the weight of an unborn child. He is clearly at least six months along.

The orderly in the corridor stops what he is doing. He has been busy filling thousands of baby bottles with milk. The milk-logged bottles tower toward the ceiling in an impossible pyramid. As the orderly straightens himself and joins the growing human barricade at the hospital room door, we see blots of milk stains on his white shirt. He, too, is pregnant.

A nurse walks by the room, just beginning to show, comforting an 8-month-old from the nursery. The child is strangely misshapen. The woman glimpses them through the tangle of limbs pressing in on her at the door to her room.

The child is swollen around its middle. Even the babies are pregnant.

The whole world is pregnant. Except for her.

The woman screams.

In the distance, a baby screams, and then another, and another, until a cacophony of infant cries overwhelms all else.

The woman collapses on the floor in the fetal position, as a mob of pregnant men, women and children crowd around her, trying to grapple with her complete otherness, the fundamental nature of her deformity.

She awakens after a long, dark sleep on a lush, green island, where a team of 25 eunuchs attends to her every whim, and even the rabbits do not procreate. And there she lives, happily ever after, for all her many more years.

Voice Over: Submitted for your approval. A young woman. Perhaps not so young, anymore. And whose fault is that? Her heart's desire led her to a peculiar place in a last-ditch effort to fit in. But who is to say what constitutes normalcy? Far be it from us to attempt such a definition, from here, in the dark recesses of the Hormone Zone.

Fade to Black . . .

The Green, Green Frog and the Blue, Blue Browns: *An Infertility Fable*

> When all else fails, one
> can always hope a frog will
> be more than a frog.

The infertile Browns get some help in their ambiguous quest for fertility from an unlikely amphibious source:

Mark and Barbara Brown were happily married for seven years. One day, Mark said to Barbara, "Let's have a baby." Barbara agreed. He kissed her gently and sweetly. They were very deeply in love. The rest should have been history—a fairy tale that ended happily ever after. But, alas, it was not meant to be so easy.

Mark and Barbara bought a house, with three bedrooms for the two children they knew would come someday. But all they got were frogs. Every night, two or three frogs from the lake across the street would congregate in front of their house. Sometimes the frogs sat around on the porch like a group of old *yentas* exchanging gossip on the stoop. Sometimes they sat on opposite sides of the garage, like sentries guarding the Brown's home. Often, they left behind impressive turds the size of a child's bowel movement. Barbara wondered if they read her morning newspaper while doing so.

One morning, Barbara was in a very bad mood, indeed, having just gotten her period. The night before, she had thought for sure that she was pregnant, and planned to take a home pregnancy test right after she had her coffee. Now, there was no need for that.

Barbara sidestepped two lumps of frog poop as she went outside for the morning paper. The frogs dove out of sight, into the jasmine and heather, with wet thrashing noises.

"Great," she thought. "No babies, just sneaky frogs, frog poop, and the possibility of contracting warts. That sums up my whole life."

She snatched the newspaper gingerly from the lawn, shaking the morning dew from its cellophane cocoon. Barbara paused to appreciate this, the quietest time of the day. The street lights were still lit. The neighbors were still asleep. The coffee was not yet brewed, the newspaper's contents still unknown.

Barbara carefully closed the front door, taking pains to corral the damp newspaper. Sometimes, in those crucial seconds, a lizard or spider or noseeum would sneak into the Brown's house, and Barbara would frantically shoo it out.

But she sensed that something had managed to creep into the foyer, and turned to see what it was.

A very fat, very green frog had followed her into the house. He squatted before her, his back to the front door.

"That's strange," she thought. "The frogs always jump away from me. They've never followed me into the house before." But this was a frog of a different color—literally. Barbara noticed that this frog was the greenest green a frog ever could be. Even in the dim pre-dawn light of the foyer, he exuded a neon aura, like a glow-in-the-dark toy.

"I know," Barbara said, opening the door to shoo him away. "If I kiss you, you'll turn into a prince. Well, I don't care if you are a prince. Get your fat slimy body out of my house," she commanded. She was in no mood for this today.

"I'm no prince," the frog replied in a reasonable tone. In fact, he sounded like Ted Koppel. "And I don't expect you to kiss me. I know I'm fat and slimy and very, very green. But I am no ordinary frog. Let me live in your bathtub for a few weeks, and you'll soon see that I am a frog of distinction and I will bring you very good luck, indeed."

Barbara had read news reports about polluted lakes harboring mutant frogs, but this was ridiculous. "I definitely need some coffee," she said out loud, and turned to go into the kitchen. She wondered if Mark was awake yet. Maybe he could get rid of the strange intruder.

"Please let me stay," said the frog, backing up a bit, so as not to seem too forward. "The lake has grown too full for an amphibian such as myself. The ducks and geese are throwing their feathers around. They think they're in charge because they can fly, as well as swim. The ducks are especially irksome— annoying beyond belief—swimming around so arrogantly with their ducklings following behind. And all that damn quacking!

"And the fish! The fish think they own the lake, just because they get to stay under water more than the rest of us. Well, I have news for them. You can't bully a bullfrog just by swimming around in schools."

Barbara thought about the frog's predicament. She understood all too well the feeling of not really belonging to the world in which one lived. All she had to do was look down the street at the "tot lot," which reminded her of her isolation and exclusion as surely as if it were surrounded by a moat.

"The owls keep me up all night with their hooting and the birds keep me up all day with their chirping," the frog was saying. "A frog needs his rest, you know. As if that wasn't enough, my in-laws just moved into a place across the bank. And," he added slyly, "I couldn't help but notice that you have a lot of empty room upstairs."

By now, Barbara decided she must be dreaming. Not wanting to wake up (she'd been having trouble sleeping lately, herself), she played along. "It's easy," she thought, "to talk to a frog in your sleep. You just keep talking, and whatever happens, happens. It's only a dream, after all."

"Won't your wife miss you, if you move in with us?" she asked, just before a yawn.

"My wife is busy with her new tadpoles," the frog explained. Barbara didn't want to correct her new dream friend and tell him that all tadpoles were new by definition.

"She doesn't need me around," the frog went on. "We hermaphrodites are quite self-sufficient. At times like these, in fact, it's very possible that we do better independently. And, as I already mentioned, I couldn't help but notice that you do have a lot of extra room upstairs."

Just then, the bedroom door opened, and Mark stepped into the upstairs hallway, shaking off the last echoes of sleep.

"Is that the exterminator?" he asked, leaning over the railing toward the front door. "What's he doing here so early?"

"No," Barbara answered, suddenly sure that she was not, in fact, dreaming. "A frog got into the house. And I think all that lack of sleep has really caught up with me."

"What? How did you let that happen?" Mark said, irritated. Now he would have to get the frog back outside. No way would Barbara touch it.

"Come here," Barbara said. "You have to see this."

Mark had grown accustomed to Barbara's strange behavior in recent months. He knew that his normally well-balanced wife was in a crazed state from the strain of infertility and its endless roulette of doctor's visits, injections and rejections—from one's own reproductive system. Reluctantly, he came down the stairs.

"Humor her," he told himself, as he did many times a day of late.

"Hello," said the frog. "This would be the master of the house, I take it? How do you do? I was just telling your wife— You are married?—that I'd really appreciate the chance to stay with you for a few weeks.

"You seem like a man who knows a smart trade-off when he sees one," the frog continued. "So here's the deal: You give me a place to stay and in return, I'll give you something that you have wanted very badly for a very long time now. Of course, there are no guarantees. But I promise, I'll do my best. Obviously, I am no average Joe frog."

Mark and Barbara looked at each other.

"He wants to stay in the bathtub," Barbara explained.

Now I know it sounds strange, but the fact is, once they got over the initial shock, Mark and Barbara rather readily accepted the sudden appearance of the neon green frog talking in their foyer. After enduring all manner of infertility treatments, two miscarriages, four surgeries and running up tens of thousands of dollars in medical bills, they had determined that just about anything could happen to them. Except, perhaps, a baby.

Their decision, then, was a strictly practical one. The frog was right. They certainly did have plenty of unused space upstairs: two empty bedrooms and a full bathroom they didn't really use, either. The frog only wanted to eat bugs and such, an aspect of the situation that appealed mightily to Barbara, who detested pests in the house. And there was the frog's promise of helping them get what they wanted most.

So that was that. The frog moved in for what he assured them would be only a brief stay. Barbara filled the bathtub with cool water, as he'd instructed.

The frog, who appeared to be larger than those who congregated on the Brown's porch every night, had no problem hopping up the steps to the second floor of the house. But he bypassed the bathroom and went instead into the guest room, plopping himself onto the sleeper sofa with an unappealing squishy sound. Barbara thought this was pretty nervy. She also wondered if it was just her imagination that the frog seemed to have grown even fatter in the few minutes since he'd entered the house.

"Don't worry," he said. "I'll be just fine here. And I will use the bathroom for its proper purposes. You just keep that tub filled, and everything will fall into place the way it's supposed to. You'll see."

Despite being a bit taken aback by the frog's sudden declarations, Barbara nonetheless felt a sense of relief that he did not venture into the other spare bedroom—the one that she and Mark always thought of as the "baby's room." For while the guest room held a cacophony of items cast off in a great jumble from other times in their lives (old dolls and purses and photographs; antiquated resumes; beach totes with clumps of sand coagulated in corner pockets) the baby's room remained relatively pristine, with but a few jackets and suitcases stored away behind the sliding closet doors.

When the house was new, Barbara used to look forward to the day when she could look out the window, across the neighboring rooftops, to the lake across the street, while changing her baby's diaper. Now she mused about the irony of owning what she referred to as a "Leave It to Beaver" house without The Beaver.

For the next three weeks after the frog moved in, Mark and Barbara went on with their lives just as if everything was normal— as normal as life can be for an infertile couple. The frog pretty much stayed to himself in the guest room, where he busied himself with knitting, of all things. Barbara thought of asking him what he was making. But since she really didn't care, she never got around to it. He seemed to get fatter and fatter. Barbara noticed that there were no bugs anywhere in the house, and ascribed his weight gain to that.

She kept the bathtub full, as the frog instructed. Over time, it became lush with seaweed, water lilies, toadstools, and the like.

Then one morning, exactly 28 days after the frog moved in

with the Browns, Barbara awoke with a strange feeling. Her period would be late. She was sure of that. But she knew she couldn't be pregnant: This was a cycle during which her doctor had told her to "take a break." And she had, no matter that it was one of the hardest things she had ever not done.

She felt inordinately bloated and uncomfortable. And nauseated. The moment she got out of bed, she felt the need to vomit, ran to the commode, and did just that.

"Honey, are you okay?" Mark called from the bed.

"Yeah," Barbara assured him. "I think I overdid the pepperoni and garlic pizza last night. That stuff was pretty greasy."

She quickly rinsed her mouth with Listerine and started downstairs to make a cup of coffee and get the newspaper. As she passed the frog's room, she saw his neon green aura glowing in the half-inch space between the bottom of the door and the bone carpet, and heard the click, click, clicking noise of knitting needles. She thought she could hear the frog humming. It sounded like Brahm's lullaby.

The smell of the coffee made Barbara feel ill all over again. So she decided to forego the coffee and have a glass of water instead. She took a prenatal vitamin out of the cupboard.

"What a farce," she thought. "Five years of prenatal vitamins must be some kind of record. If it's ever discovered that folic acid causes cancer—well, I guess if that were the case, I'd be dead by now."

She swallowed the pill and, feeling less nauseated, decided to finish the rest of the water. "Is the glass half empty, or is it half full?" she mused, as she regarded the remaining water. "I feel a little better, so maybe today it's half full," she thought. "No sense in being a total pessimist all the time."

Then, just as she was about to drink the rest of her water, she noticed what looked like a tiny fish swimming around the bottom of the glass. Somehow, this seemed perfectly natural to her.

"Put it in the bathtub," the frog advised, suddenly appearing in the adjacent family room. He seemed to have returned to his original size, but he still shone a preternatural green. And of course, there was the talking. Barbara looked more closely at the being in her glass and saw that it was actually a tadpole.

"Things don't always end up the way they begin," the frog advised. "Caterpillars turn into butterflies, of course. And tadpoles become frogs. Or do they? Do they always?"

Barbara recalled that human embryos could look just like tadpoles. As the frog suggested, she went upstairs and placed the wee tadpole in the bathtub, which now resembled a lush dark lake. The tadpole disappeared under some algae.

"Now just go on about your business," said the frog. "And let's all hope for the best. Maybe that glass really was half full."

Mark awoke upon hearing Barbara and the frog talking down the hall and joined them in the bathroom.

"What's going on?" he asked.

"We had an agreement," the frog replied. "You provided me with a much-needed break from my routine on the lake. And maybe, just maybe, I provided you with your heart's desire. But remember, there are no guarantees."

Mark peered into the bathtub just as the tadpole emerged from under a large, round leaf, a small piece of seaweed perched jauntily atop its head. They seemed to make eye contact, although Mark knew that couldn't be. But still, he felt a connection to the tadpole like none he'd known in all his 36 years.

The frog sensed Mark's blossoming hope.

"No sense asking if it's a boy or a girl," the frog cautioned. "It's way too early for that kind of thing. Why, we won't even know for three more months if it will become a frog or a baby."

And with that, the frog sprang down the stairs and out the front door.

"Good-bye and good luck!" he called, as he raced across the street toward the lake, a shiny green slash of light against the dark asphalt in the morning haze.

Mark put some clothes on and went outside to find the frog. He had a lot of unanswered questions, and he couldn't bear any more ambiguity.

Barbara went into the guest room. The frog had left it in immaculate condition. The only evidence of his stay was two pairs of booties, one blue, one pink, which he had carefully laid across the edge of the sleeper sofa. The knitting needles were gone. But he'd apparently used one of them to scratch a message into the nightstand. It said:

"Man plans and God laughs." And Barbara recognized it as a favorite saying of her father's. He had passed away just months before her first miscarriage. It seemed to Barbara that the longer he was gone, the more he was with her in all kinds of ways.

"Maybe three's the charm," she thought, turning her mind back to her miscarriages and the tadpole in the bathtub. And then she immediately imagined the frog saying, "Or maybe it's three strikes and you're out," a wet thrashing noise against her sudden optimism.

Mark sat alongside the lake across from the Brown's house. Three small boys, perhaps 9-years-old, dotted the lake's opposite bank, playing a kind of sword game with their fishing rods. He looked at them and wondered if they came from a world he would never belong to.

Mark gazed into the smooth water at his own reflection.

"I hope that isn't the only reflection of myself I'll ever have," he said. And his eyes filled with tears.

Just then, a huge bass splashed out of the lake and hovered above the water's surface. She was the same neon glowing green as the frog.

"Don't you add any of your salty human water to this lake," the bass chastised him. Mark thought she sounded like Doris Day. "This is my home and you have no right. Go home to your wife and love her and you will have a good life together, come what may. Be neither too hopeful for the future nor too fearful of it. What will be, will be."

And then she sang:

"Que sera, sera. Whatever will be, will be. The future's not ours to see. Que sera, sera."

The bass disappeared beneath the lake's surface, just as quickly as the frog had left the house only minutes before.

Mark went home to Barbara, plucking a plump, red hibiscus flower off a neatly trimmed hedge along the way. The sun had risen brightly over the houses on their block and the birds were chirping noisily in the Banyan trees that grew along their street.

"If we ever have a child," he thought as he strode down the sidewalk, twirling the flower, we'll name her "Sera."

Mark gave the big red hibiscus to Barbara, along with a kiss. She brought the flower upstairs and placed it carefully in the center of the bathtub, where it spun gently in the gathering pond. Together, they watched the petals go around and around, and tried to spot their tadpole amidst the lattice work of vegetation.

"Que sera, sera," Barbara sighed, as Mark rested his hands on her shoulders. "What will be, will be," she went on. "If we ever have a child, perhaps we'll name him Sera."

And that, they agreed, as they embraced above the cool, verdant water, was all they could know about the matter for now.

CHAPTER TEN

Happy Endings For Women
Who Can't Get (Baby) Fat And
Don't Feel Much Like Singing

Getting Over It

I don't have it all.
I may never have a kid.
No stretch marks in sight.

Imagine the last day of school, high school graduation, your wedding day and landing your dream job all rolled into one. OK. Maybe it's not quite that great. Think about when the dentist stops drilling, the rain stops raining, and your flu virus passes—to your mother-in-law, who then comes down with laryngitis.

Hard as it is to imagine, CP assures you, dear friend, that the day will come indeed when your infertility crisis will end. Perhaps you will become pregnant (in which case we may forgive you, if you're a really good friend; or we may not give a fig what you do anymore, if we never liked you in the first place). Perhaps you won't.

Perhaps you will simply decide that you've had your fill of playing lab mouse in your own very personal science experiment. Perhaps your insurance company will help you out by refusing to cover your expenses. (Lord knows, they are famously thoughtful in that regard.) Perhaps you will choose the adoption option. Perhaps you'll opt instead for many many long romantic trips for two to Italy and all the other freedoms that come with having a *really* small family.

To be sure, closure is a two-edged pregnancy test stick. It's a feeling not unlike that of losing a loved one following a prolonged illness. Yes, there's relief that the pain and suffering are over. But there is also grief for the loss you're experiencing. Allow yourself to feel both, as needed. And never stop doing the little things that will allow you to put this episode behind you and move forward with your life.

For example, you will have to decide what to do with the residue of your Perpetually Pregnantly Paused ordeal. Syringes, needles, left over "meds," "sharps" containers, and the like, needn't clutter your life and your kitchen cabinets any longer than is absolutely necessary. To be sure, an enterprising and adventurous woman might consider selling certain of these items to some gang members in a drug and crime infested area far far away from her typical haunts; or she may attempt to barter them at her neighborhood middle school, which these days is increasingly difficult to distinguish from a drug and crime infested area far far away from her typical haunts. ("*I thought this was the bake sale,*" *she might query.* "*No, ma'am; it's the bake a nail file in the cake sale,*" *a savvy freshman might enlighten her.*) Either way, this strategy entails obvious risks.

If you're a believer in Karma, go ahead and turn your surplus meds over to your infertility clinic. Alas, some poor lass may just get luckier than you did with your hormone treatments. So, you may not have a child of your own. But no hard feelings, now. You never know: Maybe your contribution will help another woman to start her long-dreamed of family. Kind of exonerates you for all those times you wished some pregnant woman's labor pains would culminate in a throng of wild rabid monkeys flying out of her butt.

Once you've purged, splurge with your spouse. Try a romantic getaway for two. Take the next few months to think about how you want to proceed—and succeed—in life. My husband and I did this very thing—and still have the credit debt to prove it. But it was worth it.

It was a few months after the last of our many IUI, IVF and I.O.U. cycles. Our final frozen embryos teetered on the brink of resolving themselves into a dew. Before we said "adieu," we settled into a penthouse, oceanfront suite in one of Florida's finest resorts, ate like pigs and drank like fish for several days. Our rooms (yes, plural), were so large that the suite had its own doorbell.

It was Labor Day weekend, so all the while, we were surrounded by—you guessed it—families with kids. God, they were obnoxious. But we learned: For us, a lifetime of seaside fun and an ocean full of rum punch would never douse our sea of sadness or bring us the happiness we sought. We'll be back, someday, we vowed, doorbell, or no doorbell, one way or another. There'll be more than two of us, somehow, and boy will we be noisy.

Getting On With It

We need closure like
we need blue skies after rain.
More sun from now on.

There is an end to the roller coaster ride from hell. There may even be a rainbow at the end of it. Is a pot of gold too much to ask for? Haven't we waited long enough? On having faith when there's no apparent reason to do so.

Ahhhh, didn't that feel good?

Now, CP wants you to know—to truly believe—that no matter what you decide and regardless of what path life will ultimately lead you down: One day, you will reclaim your kitchen cabinets; you will realize that you will never have to give yourself another injection ever again; the ungodly, unending doctor's appointments will cease; you will not care what anyone else thinks or asks; you will have your own body back, and getting a period will not feel like a death in the family. That's a CP promise. With certain ending—even apparently sad ones—ultimately, comes peace. That's a CP reality.

So, to all my fellow travelers on this lonely, twisting, uphill road: that special place—where the road curves gently downward, where pungent flowers dance in the air and land on the sidewalk beneath your feet and a canopy of branches arcs overhead—is everywhere for you, once you turn your corner.

In the meantime, keep this guide and the CP philosophy close at hand. And please, don't kill anyone—least of all yourself. That will only make matters much, much worse, and greatly diminish the odds that you will get pregnant next month, or find another way to secure for yourself a noisy, lasting peace.

CHAPTER ELEVEN

Cut-It-Out Cutouts

GET OUT
OF FAIL, FREE

Easy-To-Use Pregnantly Paused Sensitivity Training For Family, Friends and Strangers

Tear these out when you
don't want to tear your hair out.
Or someone else's.

Use these handy cut-it-out cutouts to fend off persistent queries and bromides from the various Infertility Witchdoctors and Fertile-izers you encounter. "Monopoly" has Community Chest. Infertile women are often made to feel like they have Community Uteruses. These cagey cards say "Shut Up" for you, while you maintain your savior faire, even in the midst of the beaucoup unfair:

———

True or False Test:

- It makes me feel better to hear about others who were once infertile and are now pregnant. (False—The brief, instinctive joy I experience upon learning that a new life is imminent is eclipsed by a shameful, jealous ache, faster than you can say "ova.")

- At least we're having fun trying to conceive. (False— Fighting infertility is about as sexy and romantic as having sex in a burning house. Everyone's in a big rush and the heat's in all the wrong places.)

- Infertile women always have lots of home pregnancy test kits around. (False—Infertile women are incapable of

135

refraining from using any pregnancy test that's readily available to them, home or otherwise. Don't look for logic here. There is none.)

—

Get Out Of "Fail" Free Cards

—

- See no baby. Hear no baby. Speak no baby talk. Ask no questions.

—

- I appreciate your concern, but I'd rather discuss something less personal. Like circumcision.

—

- I'm glad your:

____ friend ____ sister ____ sister-in-law ____ cousin ____ neighbor ____other became pregnant after
____ adopting ____ taking clomid ____ an IUI cycle ____ an IVF cycle
____ no longer trying to get pregnant ____ other.
But that does not:
____ change my situation ____ make me feel better
____ compel me to discuss the matter with you ____ all of the above.

—

Special Offers for the Not Knocked-Up Only!

—

F ree pass for two for a weekend get-away at Duo-Disney—
Where the world walks only in pairs. Good for as long as
you're Not Knocked-Up. Don't forget to visit us on Halloween
for Everyone is Pregnant Day! See inside for more details.
*Certain restrictions apply. No home pregnancy test kits allowed on
premises. Absolutely no pregnant women, their husbands, or children
will be admitted. Grandparents strictly prohibited. Warning: photos
of children and grandchildren are forbidden. We reserve the right
to search all personal effects to screen for offensive materials. Nuclear
family contraband will be confiscated and destroyed at management's
discretion and for the sole enjoyment of legitimate Duo-Disney guests
(tickets sold separately).*

—

You are cordially invited to join us on Mother's Day to march on
Washington for the Million Pregnantly Paused Women's March.
For slogan ideas, please refer to "Managing The Mother Of Them
All: Mother's Day," in chapter six, or use your fertile mind to
create your own personal statement!

—

Join us for a free trial visit to your local StickEnders meeting.
Free yourself from home pregnancy test tyranny. Beat unhealthy
Pregnantly Paused habits. Meet other women who can relate to
your monthly anguish. Strictly confidential. Highly effective.
"Stick With Us. We Won't Stick It To You!" For a free
consultation, or for information on meetings near your home or
office, call 1-800-UR-N-FREE.

EPILOGUE

Guaranteed Epidural-Free

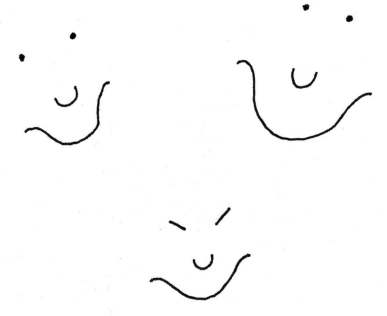

"It is better to have a hen tomorrow than an egg today."
Canned Pregnancy fortune cookie

B everly and Michael Barna adopted their daughter, Suzanna Raye Li, from China on August 12, 2001. They never looked back, except to say "Thank you" for the blessed events that brought them all together.

Printed in the United States
29612LVS00002B/1-15